The Wisdom of Old Souls

Editor
Bonita Summers

First Edition

Published by
Hidden Brook Press
writers@hiddenbrookpress.com
www.hiddenbrookpress.com

The Wisdom of Old Souls

Editor – Bonita Summers
Layout and Design – Richard M. Grove
Cover Design – Richard M. Grove
Cover Photo – Submitted by Ruth Zaryski Jackson

The cover photo was taken in 1945 and shows young Ruth with Sadie Carlton, who stayed at her mother's rooming house and was surrogate grandmother to Ruth.

Font: Footlight

Printed and bound in USA

Library and Archives Canada Cataloguing in Publication

The wisdom of old souls / editor, Bonita Summers.

Poems and prose.

ISBN 978-1-897475-12-6

1. Short stories, Canadian (English).
2. Canadian poetry (English)– 21st century.
3. Canadian fiction (English)– 21st century.
4. Grandmothers– Fiction.
5. Grandmothers– Poetry. I. Summers, Bonita, 1963–

PS8237.G73W48 2008   C810.8'035253   C2008-903275-6

With great love and appreciation

to all the wise women

who grandmothered me

into the person I am today.

Introduction

Grandmothers are our link between heaven and earth. They give us a warm place to land, helping us feel rooted within our families and inspiring us to reach for the stars with a limitless belief in the possibility of our accomplishments.

Grandmothers take the time to acknowledge us when our parents are too busy. They give us a glimpse of a past that we can only imagine through their stories. They encourage us to carry forward values and skills that would fade out of existence without their tutelage.

In this book, we celebrate the influence of older women: their wisdom and strength, the importance of their presence in our lives, and the beauty of memories we hold after their passing. Here, you will find tales of grandmothers in their youth, as they raised their children – and sometimes their grandchildren – and as they aged. What they have given us in terms of experience and understanding lasts long after they have left this world. May we all cherish the wisdom of old souls.

Editor, Bonita Summers

The Wisdom of Old Souls

Origins

Moments

Inspiration

Wisdom

Treasures

Reveries

Passages

Traces

Children

Origins

Grandmother Moon

Michael Hurley

Grandmother Moon
that's what they call you
knowing
everything's related,
everything's right here,
everyone's family.

As prayers
our hearts' incense
rise up to You
Your silvery, luminous shawl
envelops your sleeping child below
 our Mother
and in this moment
at least
there's peace,
there's silence,
the mind is quiet,
at rest,
cradled in the Great Awareness.

On a dark night
it's helpful to know
you've friends
in high places
and low,
looking over you,
supporting you.

Above, below,
when whatever your eyes see
sees you,
wherever your feet touch
touches you,
you're on your Way.
This Path
leads home.
You're among family.

And the Magic in the healing?
Even when you think
you're just lighting a little fire
to stay warm
it ends up illuminating
the whole world.

Medicine Ceremonies
are funny
that way.
Grandmothers, too.

Inspired by First Nations sculptor Garfield Thomas, whose "Medicine Ceremony" consists of two logs in the shape of a cross giving rise to a fire of purification bearing aloft twin shamans in "crazy face" masks ascending up to Grandmother Moon and Her heavens. It wasn't just that his grandma meant the world to him, but that he experienced himself in intimate relation with both the world beneath his feet and the one above his head. So each party is honoured in this equation, this sacred cosmology.

A Singular Seamstress

R.D. Roy

My own father was born
and abandoned
in 1910
his mother dying
on his arrival
his father disappearing west

And after several
Dickensian years
in a Catholic orphanage
he was taken home
by the woman
who became my grandmother

Her name was Mary Long
French Canadian seamstress
of the factories
in New England
and Eastern Quebec
Unmarried herself
breaking tradition again
adopting her son

How brave she was
standing alone
in a choice unheard of
in those times
being seen in the towns
as the unwed mother
with bastard boy in tow

And she grew a man of him
a good man
a man of conviction
and deep humanity
who returned her gift
in a life of serving others

My grandmother
the unassuming Quebecoise seamstress
never explained to me
her versions of right or wrong
but spoke clearly the lesson
the grace and the inspiration
through the choices of her life

Quilts and Quirks

Karen L. Cole

Grandma Lena spent most of her ninety-seven years in her little house near town, which looked out at the unfinished larger home that Grandpa was building when he died. She was the quintessential granny. When you entered her house, you were enticed by the tantalizing aroma of sugar cookies baking or doughnuts frying. In her dining room, next to her very busy sewing machine was a cozy little black rocker where the smaller children cuddled with her.

Grandma Lena had a curious history. Her parents divorced when she was very young – unusual for the period – and her mother sent Grandma and other siblings to an orphanage. Grandma always felt some bitterness towards her mother for giving her up to a place where she worked like a slave.

Much later, Great-Grandma married Grandpa's father, a widower with several children. Grandma's mother then brought her now teenaged children back into the family. By then, Grandpa was about to be married to a lady named Birdie. She died in childbirth the following year.

Several months after Birdie's death, Grandpa married his eighteen-year-old stepsister, Lena. Since Grandma had been away at the orphanage all those years, she and Grandpa hadn't grown up together, and Grandpa was twelve years older than Grandma. But it still seemed curious to us grandchildren when we learned of it.

Our grandparents had six children. Four of them were married and had produced five grandchildren when Grandpa died. Grandma was only fifty-three.

One of Grandma Lena's specialties was quilt making. Like many women of her time, she used the scraps from her sewing projects to create patchwork quilts. We treasured them, and every bed in our home was covered with them. Quilt making seemed an act of love, spending so many hours creating a beautiful object of art with such practical value.

In 1969, having spent several years in a convent, I had decided to leave when the school year ended. When I was home for a few days over Christmas, I went to visit Grandma Lena. She was sewing a quilt for my sister and brother-in-law who had married in October. As I watched her stitching by hand, I said, "Grandma, I love your quilts. Would you please make me one sometime?"

My Protestant grandma looked up with her big blue eyes and said gruffly, "I'll start making your quilt when I hear you're leaving the convent."

"Well, Grandma, you can start making it now, because I'll be leaving in June."

Grandma set the quilt on the couch, came over and hugged me tightly. "I'm so glad to hear it," she said. "I always thought the convent was a waste of your good brain and talents. I'll start your quilt as soon as I finish this one." I never mastered the art of quilting, but I admire it and treat my quilts from Grandma and Mother as valuable objects.

Grandma loved to pick raspberries, both black and red. They grew along the hillsides close to her place, and we kids often helped her pick. From these, she would make pies, jams, and jars of stewed berries. It always seemed fun to pick with her, because she didn't care how many we ate, and to this day I enjoy the task. Grandma Lena gathered berries into her early nineties, despite being afflicted with terrible arthritis, especially in her hands.

She often talked about arthritis, both hers and that of others. She jokingly called it Arthur, as if it had a life of its own, and she rhymed off where the affliction was located: "He's got it so bad in his neck. She's got it so bad in her hands. I've got it so bad in my feet." Genetically, she passed on this tendency too. Mine is in the early stages and, like Grandma, I'm determined not to let it slow me down.

Arthur and her children could not keep Grandma – at the age of ninety – from papering her kitchen with its complicated gables, two windows and three doorways. She babysat the neighbour boy well into her late eighties. He adored her as if she were his own granny.

Sadly, when she was ninety-four, Grandma fell and broke her hip. Although her children tried to help her stay at home, eventually she had to go into the nursing home. It broke her spirit. Her hearing had failed, and her eyesight was declining. I brought the family photograph album to trigger her memories, but she no longer could or would tell the old stories. I've always regretted that I didn't write them down sooner.

Three years later, she died. At her request, we sang "Peace in the Valley" at her funeral. She had joked that her little town of Spring Valley would be more peaceful without her around. It wasn't. Just sadder and quieter.

1918: Gram on the Danforth
Ruth E. Walker

They lumbered, she told me
down the still dirt Danforth
thick mud clung to hooves
boots, rolling wheels.

Slow steady carts and wagons
they wept down the avenue
bound to bury their dead
a dark long line.

Seen from a second-storey window
they trundled past Pape
       past the corner grocer
       past a barrel brimming
       round ripe oranges.

The doctor called
on time, prayer, and God—
she left her fever-sick mother
and wove her way
across the mire.

She carried back
three small oranges
in a brown paper wrap
       climbed the narrow
       stairs and squeezed
       spooned and
       willed God

to raise up
her Lazarus mother
as the steady stream
rolled on and passed by
down the Danforth.
Stand there today
eyes closed
heart open
to hear carts trundle past
       breathe oranges
       and the sweet drift of decay.

I Want My Grandma!
Patricia Anne Elford

There's a hole in my life. My father's mother died when he was seven; his stepmother before I was born. My mother's mother died when she was three; her father when she was seven. Two small stones set side by side into the ground of Beechwood Cemetery closed that chapter. Raised by a childless aunt and uncle, Mom remembered only snippets about her mother.

I grew up deprived. Our child-clogged neighbourhood regularly throbbed with the excitement of grandparents coming to visit. Grandmère and Grandpère, Grammy and Grampa, Nana and Grandpa, Granny and Gramps: no matter what the brand name, they were there. Not for us the excitement of a familiar car or meeting the train, with "My how you're growing!" and hugs and kisses all 'round. Everyone but my brother and I had grandparents.

Didn't I say there were a grand aunt and uncle? Yet, despite my mother's pleas, they refused to be called Grandmother and Grandfather. It would make them feel "too old". Formerly controlling and stiff in the mother substitute role, my aunt was equally as uncomfortable and severe as a substitute grandmother. The duty visits, except for some picnics at Muskrat Lake, were not enjoyed by anyone.

One day, they ended. Caught in mid-baking, my mother kept her commitment to make Halloween cookies for our school classes, instead of complying with my uncle's invitation. He'd shown up unexpectedly, asking us to go for a spin in his brand new car. I remember the flashy flip-up orange turn signals on either side. Mom admired the car and encouraged us children to go, but didn't leave the baking. The next time we heard about my aunt, we were phoned to go to Ottawa for her funeral. Not even a pseudo-grandmother remained.

But, I knew what my grandmother would have been like, if she hadn't died in attempted childbirth. The sepia picture of her as a young bride tells me that she'd have been soft-bosomed, with a just-right lap for my curling up in. She'd have had a voice like my Mom's and smelled like her cologne. She'd have worn pretty jewellery I could carefully try on, would have hugged me often, and given me little treats.

Grandma would have baked our favourite cookies. She'd have loved my brother, but would have loved me just a little bit more. Grandma would have liked that I had some of her red in my hair, and bemoaned with me our freckles and the fact that rebel wisps frequently escaped from any hairstyle attempted.

She'd have marvelled at my poems, celebrated my intelligence, been excited by my drawings, clapped for my singing, and insisted on my having good morals. She'd have struggled to teach me how to crochet and sew and knit. We'd have laughed together.

Come to think of it, my grandmother would have been very much like my mother.

Love, Sacred
Theodore Christou

You were smaller and ever cloaked in black
Forever in mourning
As many from our lands have been
Sweeping the dust of our dusty land
With a straw broom
You must have used since antiquity

The fried potatoes
That came from your kitchen
Crunched golden
Were dressed perfectly in salt
I salivate two dozen years later
And lament that I shall not
Be in your kitchen again

The pasta cooked in chicken broth
From meat you raised in the back of the yard
Has been unsurpassed in culinary history
The thick starch straws
Piled high with cheese you made
From the goats grandfather herded
Snapped against my upper lip
And I slurped them
To make you laugh
And you smiled at the sight of my dirty mouth
Despite your desire to chastise me

When we visited the holy lands
It was the first time you had left
Our little island in your ninety-odd years

Do you remember how we sat
In the shade of the grapevine
That snaked up the structure you had built

In front of your back door?
I taught you how to write your name
And your shaky hands sketched an inky image
Upon the passport that you so adored

P a n t e l i t s a

I think of home
Of Cyprus
Of the olive trees
The jasmine flowers and the blossoming almond trees
Also the poverty
The effects of millennia of colonization
Of wars and of political neglect and isolation

When the strength in your legs
And all speech had abandoned you
I could have broken too

I was merely fourteen
And my eyes became the Mediterranean
Because I could not walk with you more
By the dried-up and deserted creeks
Or across the limestone walls
That the Normans left behind

My remembrance of you is selfish

And laying flowers on your
Sacred tomb
Does not suffice
As much as a string of awkward lyrics
Balanced unevenly about your name

Moments

A Culinary Connection

J. Graham Ducker

I was worried. I was concerned for two connected reasons: yesterday my master chef, Henri, buried the grandmother who had raised him from infancy; and I was apprehensive that the entrees at The West Bank Experience – Fine French Cuisine – would not be up to standard.

At four o'clock, I unlocked the main door, although I knew most patrons would not arrive until after seven. I glanced into the kitchen. It was obvious my portly and usually jovial cook was hurting, as he seemed overly critical of everything Charles, his apprentice, attempted.

I was about to intercede when a diminutive senior lady entered the foyer.

"Are you open?" she asked.

"Why, yes we are. Won't you come in?"

"I don't know if I should." Her eyes flashed. "It looks expensive." She looked at her hands. "I was just looking for a place to have a quiet cup of tea."

"We can handle that," I invited. "Are you hungry?"

Multi-ringed fingers tightened on her beaded cloth purse. "Heaven knows I should be," she started, "but ever since Phil's funeral, I haven't been able to eat a thing. My stomach just knots up, if you know what I mean."

"How long were you married?" I ventured.

There was a tiny chuckle. "Oh my, I've been a widow for years. No, my grandson was killed in a car crash a few days ago and …"

She began fishing in her handbag.

I snatched a cloth napkin, handed it to her and waited.

After dabbing her eyes, she looked up. "I'm sorry. I shouldn't be bothering you with my troubles."

"Not at all," I smiled, gently taking her elbow and leading her to an isolated corner. "There is a cozy little table right over here."

I motioned to one of the waiters. "Would you please bring this lady a pot of tea? I want to talk to Henri." Leaving her in capable hands, I hurried into the kitchen where I put my arm around Henri's broad shoulders.

"Henri, my friend, how would you like to apply your personal expertise to a special customer?"

His immaculate moustache twisted with the quizzical look he gave me.

"Don't worry about the menu," I assured him. "It will be slow for a while yet, and Charles is quite capable of looking after the few customers."

Curiosity showed in Henri's face as I led him to the door. "Come and meet her."

The elderly woman put down her teacup and smiled as we approached.

"Henri," I began, "This is …?"

"Mrs. Harrison." she finished. "Doris Harrison."

"Mrs. Harrison, this is Henri, our chef."

As they shook hands, I addressed Henri. "Mrs. Harrison has not had much of an appetite for the past few days."

I pulled a chair out, indicated for him to sit down, and then I turned to the woman. "Mrs. Harrison …" I started.

"Doris. Please call me Doris."

"Okay, Doris, if anyone can cure a missing appetite it is Henri here. I have to go, but I'll let you explain why you have not been eating."

I patted Henri on the shoulder. "Don't worry about the kitchen. Charles and I will take care of things."

I went to the bar where the staff agreed to steer customers away from that area.

The corner-table drama unfolded. Tentative at first, the two heads soon bent closer as the intensity increased. She dabbed her eyes while he patted her hand; then later, she dabbed his eyes and patted his hand. No one dared to refill the teapot.

I was helping Charles with the devilled lobster canapés when Henri, beaming like a little kid, burst into the kitchen.

"Mon Dieu, she is like my own Grandmère! And she is starving! I shall make for her the perfect dinner – Red Snapper with Lemon Marjoram Butter."

Once again, Henri was in fine form. He was soon brushing marjoram butter over two broiled filets framed by roasted potatoes and baby carrots.

"Some Chablis Grand Cru would go well, eh?" he winked.

"I'll get it," I laughed.

As I poured their wine, it was obvious the dinner was secondary to the connection across the table. I left the bottle in the ice bucket.

Much later, as I was helping Charles with the Cauliflower Crostini hors d'oeuvres, Henri strolled in.

"Helas, she has gone home," he sighed, and then wagging his finger, he continued, "But you know, I think she will be back."

"Of course," I teased, "She likes your cooking."

Henri remained serious. He took my hand. Tears welled in his intense eyes. "Thank you, my friend. I shall never forget this." He continued to grasp my hand.

I could only nod, manage a weak smile, and swallow hard.

Finally, he dropped my hand, walked over to Charles and smiled. "So now, mon ami, how is that bouillabaisse coming along?"

From the Rocking Chair

Bonita Summers

I cannot forget Grandma's farm. At its centre, the kitchen, where activity revolved around a braided rug with a small dog, Fido, resting upon it, and a caged bird who seemed to echo Grandma's nasal "Allo" when the phone rang and the room pulsated with food and people, and the old rocker from where I witnessed the stories and laughter of the farmhands at the long table, and just outside, the wonder, oh, the wonder to chase the hens and discover warm beneath, their eggs with hearts still beating inside.

I cried when one dropped from my hand and blood ran on the ground. Still, there was forgiveness and freedom for a little girl whose life was not gilded and who came to the Quebec farmhouse each year for a brief spell of kindness and a pinch of the magic that never left me.

Gatherers

(Great-Grandma Lily & Great-Aunt Julia)

Kathryn MacDonald

Bending over berry brambles
scent rises, surrounding me
with summer's perfume,
rich and sweet.

Long ago, I followed two old women
picking wild fruit:
blackberries, red raspberries, gooseberries
along the liminal path
between the railroad track
and my father's fields.
In their garden, they gathered
red and black currants into baskets.
Summer fruits, all these,
lush and ripe with life and love.

Is it subliminal yearning that has led me here
where wild berries also grow along fence rows
bordering another railroad track
that cuts through another parcel of land?
Here, wild strawberries fringe pastures
and fields of native grasses,
like waves rippling timeless shores.
Here, I am growing old,
following in the wake of ancestors.

Now, it is me tending currants and raspberries,
filling baskets, harvesting memories
as old as time, as steady as seasons
discovering thresholds of memory anew.

Grandmother's Children
K. V. Skene

Outside the kitchen, laughter
rattles the pane. A day
to be listened to
as grandmother's children torch
the backyard, feast
on heat, the sweet-stickiness of it.
Call them in
and they swim out of the leaf-green,
pull her under
the weight of their eyes, little
gap grins, the soft bluish colour
of their napes where damp curls dribble
the forbidden odour of pondwater. A mosquito bite
excites instant attention, then
strawberry ice cream spooned out of round brown bowls,
that Sunday
last summer.

Routines and Recurrences
(a pantoum)
D. S. Martin

At ninety-six she's seen here all she'll see
She's learned to laugh at her own confusion
Her days fill with routines and recurrences
It's as though her memory has become full

She's learned to laugh at her own confusion
She can't remember taking her walk today
It's as though her memory has become full
She can't keep track since each day's much the same

She can't remember taking her walk today
Details of those who love her slip away
She can't keep track since each day's much the same
Someone she doesn't recognize speaks her name

Details of those who love her slip away
Her days fill with routines and recurrences
Someone she doesn't recognize speaks her name
At ninety-six she's seen here all she'll see

Inspiration

Grandma Walks Beside Me
Ellen Curry

In the year 1933, there was a large increase in serious crime in Salisbury, Rhodesia (now called Harare, Zimbabwe). The government decided to build a state-of-the-art prison, complete with a hanging platform and electric chair.

Along with the jail, new houses were built for the staff. When my father was promoted to Chief Superintendent of the prison, our family was allocated the largest home, with six bedrooms and a magnificent three-sided-porch. In Africa, with the scorching hot sun, a very large porch was invaluable on a house. Being three-sided, the chairs could be arranged and rearranged for sun, shade, and light breezes according to the weather. It was the perfect place to sit quietly, knit and sew baby clothes, or just idle away the hours sipping on a long cool glass of lemonade, watching the wild animals drink from the watering hole at the end of the game park, which bordered the prison grounds.

As we had so much room, it was decided that my maternal grandma would come to live with us. Grandma's favourite pastime was making pretty clothes for her long-awaited first granddaughter. Had I been born triplets, there still would have been more than enough dainty matching outfits to go around. Everyone knew that I was going to be a girl, because a wedding ring tied to a piece of string and dangled over my mother's pregnant stomach went round and round in a circle. Had it gone straight from side to side, my mother and grandmother would have been very disappointed, as there were already two boys in the family.

There were some unusual happenings at our house the three weeks between Grandma dying and me being born. The first was the ambulance taking Grandma's body away one Sunday, and the last, two Sundays later, was the ambulance bringing the midwife to our house for my birth because her car had broken down.

I grew up uncannily like my grandma. At the age of five, when my girlfriends were playing with their dolls, I would sit for hours on the porch, knitting scarves for the overseas troops and making all my own dolls' clothes. Sewing and knitting came easily. I could not read a knitting pattern, but my mother would just have to show me once and I understood.

I grew up hearing, "You are just like your grandma" and "Missy, don't you give me that superior look. You are just as obstinate and stubborn as your old Dutch grandma."

On my twelfth birthday, I was given a letter that my grandmother had written to me just a few days before her death. That letter was my most prized possession; I read it so many times that I knew it by heart. She wrote –

"My precious darling Madelena, (which is my middle name and Grandma's first name)

You will never be alone, because I will always be with you in your heart. Our souls are one. Treat people the way you want them to treat you. When you start something always finish it – winners never quit and quitters never win. Never be afraid to try new things. That is how you learn, and you will have some interesting experiences. You can do anything you want to do; you don't know if you don't try. When you sit on the porch and knit or sew with your fingers, use your brain and think and plan what you want to do and how you are going to do the task. Just remember that I am always with you, because you are my very special little girl."

During one of my many arguments with my brother, he tore up my grandma's letter and dropped it into the fire. I was so upset, I lay on the bed and cried until my pillow was wet. That was the first time that I heard my grandmother's voice; it was soft and warm, but with a thick Dutch accent.

She said "My precious Madelena, why are you crying? That was only a letter. Can't you feel me beside you holding your hand? You know that I will never leave you."

Grandma has been my constant companion since, always encouraging me to try new things. I will hear her say, "Go on, you can do it. Don't be afraid."

Grandma also told me about travelling in a covered wagon. She was pregnant with her fourth son, and the journey was arduous. They encountered unfriendly natives and wild animals along the way. Water and food were scarce, and she had to cook over an open fire. The trip took seven long months, and she needed all her strength and tenacity just to survive the journey.

They settled on a farm that Cecil John Rhodes had given them in the Eastern district of Rhodesia, where the soil was rich, water was plentiful, and crops, vegetables and fruit trees grew in abundance. She used to make preserves and knit and sew for the church bazaars. This was her way of giving back to the community.

At the age of sixteen, I started to do volunteer work with the Red Cross to give back like Grandma. With this attitude, my life has been anything but boring. In 1961, I heard about black people in Kenya being ordered to kill white people they worked for or be killed. I did not want my children to grow up in a world full of racism, so we made the move from Africa to Canada, and Grandma came with us. Sometimes when I had doubts, I would hear, "My precious, you have done the right thing. Remember that I am always with you."

After I had been a school secretary for ten years and felt that I needed a challenge, I opened a scuba diving store/school - Innerspace Dive Store in Oshawa. Once again, Grandma was there leading me on. The store was doing very well, and I had six diving instructors working for me. I was able to take diving trips all over the world with customers.

It was a lot of fun working with mostly young people, but putting in long hours at the store was starting to wear on both me and my husband. I decided to put the store on the map to attract buyers. At the age of forty-six, I set a Guinness World Record by staying underwater for sixty-eight hours. I had no trouble selling Innerspace for a good price.

Gone was the porch-sitting with knitting needles and sewing. I was enjoying being active. I painted the inside of our house from door to door, and then took up golf, the most humbling of games. Again, there was Grandma, "O.K. let's hit this ball straight; no, not in the bunker or the rough again. We can do this. Let's concentrate. It's not that hard."

I have always loved the water. So when I heard about a seven-day white-water rafting trip down the Colorado River in the Grand Canyon, I was ready, no matter that I did not know another soul going. What did I care? Grandma was with me.

The following year, taking a mule train trip, I could not resist returning to the most quiet, peaceful place in the world. In the Grand Canyon, you find yourself whispering, as though you are in a huge cathedral. Grandma did not enjoy the mules; it reminded her of the trek she had made as a young woman, from South Africa to Rhodesia.

In the year 2000, I decided to mark the millennium with a bicycle trip through Austria, Switzerland, and Germany. We both loved the freedom of being able to bike through the countries, stopping to talk to people along the way. Although we travelled 290 kilometres in three weeks, we had lots of time to enjoy the sights – buildings hundreds of years old, castles, churches, and monasteries. Grandma felt very comfortable being back in Europe. She led us along some paths that were not on the map; we saw covered bridges, little stone cottages with old-fashioned gardens, and one hidden garden at the end of an overgrown pathway, which had wild flowers the likes of which we had never seen before. Our guide believed in angels, and he was sure that I was being led by one. I knew it was Grandma having the time of her life showing me around her old stomping grounds.

Grandma has taught me many lessons during the sixty-odd years she has walked beside me, and there is no doubt that she is responsible for my being the adventurous person that I am today.

Grandma Tells Me Stories

A Dub Performance Piece
Bonita Summers

Grandma on my shoulder
from a family full of writers
knew her granddaughter
had her own tales to tell.

When young, my gran was silenced,
but in death far more defiant,
said, "In life, I wish I'd raised a little hell."

Grandma on my shoulder
knows her granddaughter is bolder
tells her stories now
while she has tongue to tell

'bout the vicious and seditious
ways of keeping little girls at bay
and teaching them to swallow
all their rage.

For it's gotta come out somehow
and you know it will, 'cause right now
all those angry words
are soaking up the page.

Now, dead women cannot tell their tales
except to kin who listen close.
Sad to say, the ones alive are oft
more silent than the ghosts.

Yet, Grandma tells me stories.
Ya, she whispers in the night,
picks the odd time that my own dreams
don't shake me awake in fright.

It's too bad she couldn't shout them
to our Mafioso family,
how she wanted something more
than what she was told she oughta be.

Yet, it's easy to be silenced
by the constant fear of rape or death
and the way you learn to live with them
by scarcely drawing breath.

But I'm breathing full, so long away.
They've lost my scent. The dogs don't bay.
The hunt is off.
I'm dead to them it seems …

Can't get me now
I scream and howl.
I'm obvious, full cheek and jowl
corporeal, and dropping words in reams.

My mom I'm not, who pens her stories
romance novels, violent glories
men on women; women lose to men.

In her quiet collaboration
giving in to degradation,
surely, dead she is in voice
in league with them.

Too often turning other cheek
it's not the quick but dead who speak
and those inheriting earth are meek
and Mother Earth herself is weak.

So, be the quick in mind and tongue.
Oh, tell your tales while you are young.
For if you wait till life is through,
who will you tell your stories to?

Mary Murchison McLeod
Winona Baker

"How living are the dead." Florence Coates

Sometimes when mother was trying
to make a meal out of not much, or find
something we could wear to school
she'd angrily sigh, then say

*If your grandmother was still alive
you girls would have a much better life*

She didn't mean her mother
our faraway grandma in Ontario
She meant her mother in law
Mary Murchison McLeod
who died years before I was born

Wished mother wouldn't say that.
The sentence usually signalled
a stressful soliloquy starting
I'd tell him ...

*You have family now— before you make speeches
for Dr. Bethune in China , learn
how to talk to your own sons ...*

*Before you collect for brigades in Spain
make sure your children have something
to put in their lunch buckets ...*

Sometimes I'd go alone
to the front room and stare
at Grandma's sepia portrait
in its large oval frame

Thought— if I gaze long enough
at her strong, calm face can I learn
how to make us a better life

Wisdom

The Crazy Wisdom
of Grandma Nuthin
for Kay Hurley who was nothing
like your idea of her

Michael Hurley

"Crazy wisdom is the wisdom of the saint, the Zen master, the poet, the mad scientist, and the fool. Crazy wisdom sees that we live in a world of many illusions, that the Emperor has no clothes, and that much of human belief and behaviour is ritualized nonsense. Crazy wisdom understands antimatter and old Sufi poetry; loves paradox and puns and pie fights and laughing at politicians. Crazy wisdom flips the world upside down and backward until everything becomes perfectly clear."

> Wes "Scoop" Nisker
> author, stand-up comic,
> meditation instructor,
> born-again-and-again Buddhist

"Among the great things which are to be found among us, the being of nothingness is the greatest."

> Leonardo da Vinci

Grandma was an old woman who taught me nothing — not so much howta live as how to let go figurin' it all out and get on with it, get into it, get down and dirty in the mess and mystery, nothing but being, fully, completely, right here, right now.

"Where else could you possibly be," she'd laugh. Then point to my head. Yeah, guess you can get lost in there pretty fast sometimes, thinking inside that box Jack built and you bought inta, even before you knew it. "Comes with the territory, honey. Don't take it personal. Take it easy."

Granny herself was empty sky most of the time. Endless, vast expanse of blue and void. Shining, resplendent. No clouds stuck to her. No birds broke their flight and fell. Nothing but the heavens on earth.

A sorta river, flowing both ways — that was Gran. Neither pushin' nor pullin,' she just let you be, let you be yourself, the self you'd be when nobody was about, or when you got around to letting go, deep-sixin' any fancy ideas what a self was or could be, might be, should be.

"What you need a self for anyway," she'd wink when I was caught on a stick somewhere in my mindstream. Granny'd smile then, from ear to ear, always laughing, like mountains was molehills, and that old house of cards I'd be fussin' and frettin' over would come tumbling down, gloriously, leaving standing just the Joker. Granny knew her card tricks.

She was a thief, too. And a damn good one. She'd steal your certainty, your Rules and Regulations, Secret Codes and Hiding Places, your precious notions of how it all should be, 'til there was nothing left of you neither, naked as butt-bare Lear. And nothing left to hide. From or in. Stole all yer stuff, all that baggage you'd been hauling around for eons, maybe not even knowing it. Then she gave you back only what is. She was a rascal that way. But you knew where you stood with Granny — on the edge. Your edge. Knees knockin', mind trippin' all over itself, like somersaults gone bad. And by God with a big grin she'd push you over — and you flew.

Jailbreak and re-creation — that was Granny's forte. Escape artist extraordinaire. Rolemodelin' daring escapades and hairpin escapes from whatever shit you'd managed to stir up for yourself this time round. Like, here's your wings, goofus, right where they've always been, now smarten up and fly straight. And keep it simple. Jesus H. Krishna! Save the loop-dee-loops 'til yer next incarnation, Swami.

I always remember Granny in starlight and sunlight. She never kept the curtains closed. Foolishness, she said. And no one was more of a fool than her (she'd say that too), being so wide open to it all. Her door was always open. You never knew who'd she'd be entertaining. Sadness? Joy? Nobody got turned rudely away; nobody overstayed their welcome. They're all family, she'd say, even anger (knowing that particular visitor always riled and discombobulated me). The more I slammed the door on the bastard, the more I found I'd somehow locked him inside. "Easy does it, sonny, no needta get yer shorts in a knot, and get all heated up. Leave it be, and that hot-under-the-collar feelin' will morph into some cool fireworks, dude. Chill."

She didn't much believe in curtains or veils, concrete bunkers or lock-downs. You'd sit there, stewing about something or other, knowing she'd twig to that in half a nanosecond and knowing that's why you'd come in the first place. There you were about to turn to cinder, and Granny would somehow abort the combustion process while keeping the spontaneous aspect alive and kickin', and you'd realize there weren't much between that fearless woman and anything else in the universe. There was always a fresh breeze blowing in her place. And it could caress and soothe you or blow you away, and only she'd know which way it was blowin' in that particular instant.

This one time I was having a mega-meltdown over something or other, drowning in my melodrama, afraid the sky was falling, again. Sometimes, Gran would play Rescue Squad and bail me out, hopin' I'd catch on eventually to how to do it for myself, how to override my own wound-up-too-tight circuits. This time, I'm coming up for air, a rare moment for moi, and by God she pushes me back down, like, ok, you're really milking this one for all it's worth, go ahead, bite into it big time. She pushes me down again into my depths until, sink-or-swim time, there was nothing for it but either curl up fetal-hobbit on the very bottom of my brainpan forever and get it the fuck over with, or ... learn to swim in the Mystery.

My choice: cave in, crash land in ye olde mind somewhere, or just sort of let go, shift gears, climb down from the Control Tower and check out the terrain from a different angle. Which somehow I did, courtesy of Granny's kick in the butt. Kicked outta my mind into ... nothing? Sort of, but not mindfear panic-nothing. Into what Granny calls (when she calls it anything) The Emptiness. Entered into, it would seem, when head melts into heart and finds itself cradled all the while in Awareness, this vast sea ya can't drown in cuz you are it. And always have been. Surprise! And there's only One of it, or us, or whatever It is. Kinda short-circuits words, eh, when they get too close to It and just fizzle out. Call in the poets and singers!

So Grandma was fierce grace, letting you roast on your own spit until you got so hot and sweaty you were damn well ready to climb down by yourself. She'd kind of tweak whatever situation you found yourself floundering around in 'til you discovered the breathing holes for yourself.

Gran never tried to "teach" you nothing, tho. That wasn't her style. She'd have that invisible wand of hers out, waving it about in your face where it would be the last place you'd see it cuz we're always so frickin' busy looking anyway but here and now for our lost goodies. A wave or two, and stuff would just more or less fall into place. A little sleight of hand and heart was not beyond her. And you could ask that woman anything. And get an answer. Or not get an answer. Which in itself was an answer of sorts, maybe just the one you needed, maybe questioning your question in the first place. Or maybe not. You hadta be on yer toes, do your own homework. Gran was no slouch in this game, and didn't tolerate louch players on her court.

Granny never lied. Never told "THE TRUTH" either, at least the kind some Special Inside Trackers think they own. And are happy to dispense for a fee. Nothin' came with pricetags attached at Gran's place. Even that lightbulb flashin' over your suddenly illuminated head: "don't go grabbin' after it, sonny, you'll only hide the light that way. Let go of it, now, and see what ya see." Before the dark night of the soul was thru, she somehow or other brought it about that you couldn't help but stumble over your own truth, again and again, 'til it was impossible even for you to ignore any longer. Brought you face-to-face with Original Face. Right into Presence.

So she taught you nothing, nothing you didn't already know, somewhere deep inside, but just couldn't get to at that moment, cuz you were too busy not being in the moment. Too preoccupied reviewing yer past hits, runs and terrors, or worrying yourself sick about some imagined shit about to come down in the future. You'd be battening down the hatches while she was a colourful prayer flag, blessing the wind that buoyed her up and blew you away.

I believe in nothing, Granny'd tell you, with a wink. I like nothing. I like nothing so much as nothing. Nothing catches my fancy. Nothing matters. Nothing's worthwhile. Nothing bears thinkin' about. And nothing is what you think it is. Scientists say there's no thing out there, no thing separate from all things. Mystics say there's nobody home inside here, no single thing you can call your self, separate from all else. Nothing's what it's cracked upta be. Nothing I know of. Nothing changes. Nothing's permanent. Nothing's forever. It all amounts to nothing. Nothing's too much for me!

Nothing phased Granny. She danced it all. The good, the bad, the ugly. Light on her feet cuz she took herself lightly. Never collected nothing. Just gave it all away. Until she had more than she began with. Things is funny that way. Her hands were empty, but they were capable of offering you anything. Offer you the world, the world outside your skimpy version of it. That's how she fed us. Nobody walked away from her hungry. We thought she was dirt poor; she counted herself wildly rich. We thought she might get lonely; she felt everybody was family. We told her we had big plans; she said we had baggage. When we showed her where to look, she suggested we get our eyes checked. When we tried to take her places, show her a good time, she simply folded her legs, closed her eyes, said she'd see us in that blissful interstellar space between two thoughts, that magic moment of orgasm between incarnations, between scripts, mental maps, before and after, right and wrong.

When we tried to pin her down, Granny'd run circles round us. You just could not catch up to her—except by standing still, cooling your jets wherever you were, wherever she found you. She'd sit still then, so still at the quiet centre of the 3 worlds, curled round something vast, like a gnarled old oak root. Grandma was forest, stretchin' from here to the horizon. The kind you could disappear into for days, emerging on some other shore, unrecognizable to yourself, to a mind grasping for a foothold other than where you found yourself, other than right here. It felt great somehow, torched in the fire of an incandescent NOW and you could lose it just by grabbing after the flimsy straws of yesterday or tomorrow.

Sometimes, I'd look over at Granny and see nothing but a coyote. Howling away, at a moon that wasn't there.

Granny died. Like everyone and everything else, Grandma died. Got up the next morning and got on with her life. She was funny that way. Leaving no forwarding address, leaving us nothing save the impression she'd somehow uplevelled us, her disappearing act a Cheshire Cat Smile that seemed to say, Okay, you want me—now find me. Remember, there's just one of us. Just Awareness. So where could I go?

As Gran always said
(to no one in particular)
she was nobody
special
nothing
more
nothing
less
nothing
at
all

    and now
    nothing
    makes sense
    to me

Identity

Kathryn MacDonald * see author's note p. 110

I am all the grandmothers:
French, English, Irish, and
the Wyandot woman
who was born on an island in Big Marsh.

I am Sky Woman
    falling, falling into an abyss
    without knowledge that I will be saved
    by muck becoming island on a turtle's back.
I am grandmother moon
    a soft and gentle light
    a light reflecting sun
    a light dancing on water, shimmering on snow.
And I am the earth goddess
    mother of all life.
I walk the circle of my life,
    past becomes future.
My life becomes my children
    and grandchildren.
My seeking leads me toward a future I
    cannot imagine, through a past cast in shadows.
And I walk, circling like the moon circles earth,
    like earth circles sun.
This dance spins a thread
    weaves a cloth
    whose pattern shapes my life
    tells my story.

                "Who are you?" someone asks.
                "I am the story of myself,"
                comes the reply.
        —   so says the Kiowa poet.

I am the story of the grandmothers.
I am becoming the story of grandchildren.

Planting Seeds in my Spiritual Garden: Grandmothers as Witnesses of Joy

Carolyn Hei-Kyoung You

When I try to picture the distance between my hometown of Sault Ste. Marie, Ontario, Canada, and where my grandma lived in Seoul, Korea, I imagine drilling a hole right through the globe. My grandma lived on the other side of the world.

My maternal grandparents' first visit to Canada happened when I was six. During this visit, my grandpa asked me again and again, "Guess what my favourite number is" to which he would reply with his signature childlike enthusiasm, "SIX!" As persistent as my grandpa was in this endearing line of questioning, my brother and I reportedly had our own question: this one for my grandma. She fried up such delicious crispy French fries that we often asked her when she would make them again. And the answer kept coming back: "little later, little later …" So, my grandma's nickname was born: "little later grandma".

A few years after that visit, my grandparents made a second trip to Canada. By this point, my family had moved to a different house, one that stood out for its unusual architecture. Among its unique features were the wooden garden boxes that sat adjacent to the uneven stairs that led up to our orange-red front door. My mom, who is an avid gardener, and who has always had an eye for beauty, had filled the little boxes with assorted flowers and shrubs: deeply coloured purple plums with tiny pink and white blossoms, and burning bushes, which, though usually green, were so named for their ability to suddenly ignite into brilliant red.

I had heard the Biblical story of the burning bush, and I knew on the inside the crimson red of shame. Nothing was good enough for this god who sat in constant judgment of His creatures. I learned to fear the spectre of a deity who announced Himself through messengers that burst into flames. So I was rather puzzled and taken aback when, as Grandma looked out admiringly at the colourful garden boxes my mom had planted, she remarked to me, "God was so good to us, giving us flowers and all the beauty of creation to enjoy."

The distance between this image of God and the one that I had formed in my mind and heart seemed greater than the distance between my and my grandma's respective home-lands. Yet, her words planted a seed in the garden of my spiritual life, and the quiet joy with which she spoke radiated sunshine on that garden. In the years that followed, I left home and unceremoniously left the church. Outside the church, I found my spiritual sustenance through U2 lyrics and literary texts replete with Biblical allusions and spiritual themes. It was not until later that I realized these sources had fed a soul yearning that had been with me from an early age.

The possibility of joy rooted in the recognition of goodness – in God, in creation, in myself, and in others – all of this lay dormant in the seed that my grandma had sown. Carrying this seed in my heart, I put down roots in two spiritual communities: First United Church and L'Arche Ottawa, which proved to be fertile ground for the seed to sprout.

There was no shortage of rain during this season of spiritual searching. Bono's tortured voice spit out the words: "Across the field you see the sky ripped open, see the rain through a gaping wound." I released red hot tears of shame that, if searing, were also cleansing. Mercifully, there were many gifted healers who wrapped my wounds with great care and tenderness.

In time, tender green shoots pushed their way through the ground, and it occurred to me that it might be worthwhile to cultivate my garden, cutting away old growth to give new life a chance to flourish. Instead of a hankering for my grandma's homemade French fries, I was overtaken by an insatiable hunger for soul food. I decided to undertake formal theological studies at Queen's University in Kingston.

In truth, this process felt less like cultivation and more like conflagration. I was to learn the meaning of the words: "If you walk amid the burning flames, you shall not be harmed." The inner fire seemed hell-bent on razing my garden to the ground, but it turned out to be a purifying and transforming force. I entered my studies with spiritual curiosity; I graduated with a stronger sense of myself as a seeker, and with an emerging vision of myself as a spiritual resource for others.

* * *

Another seed was planted in my spiritual garden by my uncle's mother who is known to me as "Eugene's grandma", Eugene being my uncle's eldest son. (There is a custom in Korea that relatives are named in relation to the eldest child in the immediate family. Traditionally these names, which can seem unwieldy to Western ears, are used instead of a person's first name.)

Every time Eugene's grandma saw me, she would wrap her arms around me and squeeze me so tight I sometimes wondered if she might break one of my bones. This gesture was accompanied by a long exclamation of joy, and a smile broad enough to span the distance between Canada and her native land. Though she did not have words to communicate with me, this characteristic greeting spoke clearly of her love for me.

The strength that she expressed through her embrace was also shown through her remarkably active daily life. When she lived with Eugene and his family, she could often be found in the kitchen stirring up a pot of Korean jjigae, or stew. Her concoctions filled the whole house with the pungent smell of fish, or of kimchi, that classic Korean side dish of spicy fermented cabbage. Though she sometimes complained of being tired, her fatigue was not enough to take away her smile, which sparkled from the silver fillings in her mouth. She had the look and feel of a favourite leather shoe: lines well worn from years of walking on life's path, and leather stretched and softened to fit just right.

Years later, a conversation between my mom and I turned to Eugene's grandma, whom my mom mentioned was a Buddhist. She recalled Eugene's grandma's remark that life was so surreal, it seemed like a dream. I wondered: was there some connection between Eugene's grandma's capacity for joy and her sense that life was merely a dream?

It was only years later, towards the end of my theological studies that the seed Eugene's grandma had planted began to sprout. As my interest in Eastern religious traditions emerged, I began to see the connection between one's capacity for joy, and one's realization of life's dreamlike, impermanent quality.

Having some awareness that everything passes has helped me to appreciate the moment, because this is where life is. Right now, in the full engagement of the senses. I have learned that this quality of wakefulness brings me joy, and it is there, as a free gift of grace, in every moment of my life. It is up to me to claim this joyful awareness – not just for myself, but so I can share it with others.

Though my interactions with them are few in number, both my maternal grandma and Eugene's grandma have been vital influences on my spiritual life.

My maternal grandma sowed the seed of joy to be found in goodness, which helped me to see the Christian tradition in which I was first rooted in a new light that brought comforting and life-giving warmth to my spiritual garden. Eugene's grandma nourished my interest in Eastern religious traditions, and planted the seed of joy to be found in awareness.

I am grateful to each of these grandmothers as my witnesses of joy. Through them, I have been inspired to claim for myself some of the life-sustaining elements of their respective religious traditions. For all the many differences between these traditions – and between these grandmothers – it is striking to me that what connects them is joy. Or as another cherished elder woman in my life has aptly put it, "different traditions, the same glory."

Treasures

Grannie's Magic Thimble

Louise O'Donnell

In my picture book,
a fairy drank from a magic thimble.
Grannie didn't believe in magic.
And no fairy could drink from Grannie's thimble.
It had no bottom, or top.
It was a wide silver band with tiny indentations
that fit around the end of her finger.
But I thought Grannie's thimble was magic,
the way she guarded it.
She kept it in a special box
in a special drawer
in her sewing machine.
Grannie said it was special because
to sew using Grannie's thimble
you had to guide the needle through the cloth
with the side of your finger.
Novices, she said, plunged the needle
with the top of their finger
creating gross sloppy stitches.
Grannie guided her needle the way
an artist guides her brush,
producing fine stitches,
invisible even on a gossamer gown.
Rich ladies came to Grannie
because of her stitches
and because of her magic with a style, they said.

I couldn't master Grannie's magic.
No fine stitches from my fingers.
But for her sake,
I struggle to stitch together
the slant angled magic of words.

What Remains Hidden

Bonita Summers

My love for all things hidden began with the bracelet Gran
gave Mom that would be mine when I turned 16 and how
Mom would take it out when I asked just to see for a
moment, to hold in my little-girl hand the charms that
opened to show a couple inside a church getting married, a
baby in a bassinet, the Lord's Prayer in a tiny Bible … and
such surprise that these were tucked away inside until I
sought them, like the voices that disappeared when I
listened too hard and the faces on the periphery that
dissolved when I turned toward them … and this drove me
to seek the hidden, to plumb the woods for pathways
unexplored, to open every book for stories unknown, to ask
the universe inside me every question, because of all that I
could see that was hidden from others; I had to understand
or die in the trying … and all of this, all of this, because
Gran, you took your secrets with you, knowing I had the
Gift like you and those before, and letting your fear prevent
you from telling me what you knew and how to live in a
world with those who curse the unknown and would call
me a witch before I learned that some things should remain
hidden.

Emily's Rocking Chair
Rebecca Luce-Kapler

The rocking chair from great-aunt Emily sits
in your living room   square and solid like her
you can fit your arms into the groove

    remember what you cannot imagine
    escape from a distant country
    a religion no longer welcome
    one forbidding conflict, alcohol, dice

    and quiet devotion to a god you cannot hear
    a stern and joyless man who stopped you
    from dancing, from laughing aloud
    from twirling your crinoline to swish
    your full skirt into a frenzy of knees, panties

    the deep reading of scripture
    a reverence for the scholar, a thread
    that now traces your life, a singular passion
    for the development of mental fortitude

Emily's rocking chair a gift from her wedding
    ten years later   her husband died working for the CPR
    some kind of train wreck
    a pump car rolling over his legs
    so he bled out

you don't remember which part of the story is true
    except that he died
    and that it's the same railroad Emily's family travelled
    in their flight from Russia

the train her daughter Edith took to the hospital
    for her lobotomy
    who decades later at your cousin's shower
    gave a sympathy card
    and a Sunlight detergent box full of old kitchen gadgets
    egg slicer, spatula, box top cutter

Edith's always saving things, Emily told your grandmother
    by way of apology
    she could no longer care for her daughter or herself
    and their names floated to the top of the waiting list
    a shared bedroom like the last sixty years
    but smaller

Edith thinks we are going to a hotel, Emily said
    then asked her sister to find a home
    for the rocking chair   the square and solid
    where you now sit remembering
    as it trembles with vibrations
    from the eleven o'clock train

Grannie and the Bicycle

Louise O'Donnell

It was blue,
a CCM,
with real rubber tires.
That's why it was so expensive.
Wartime. Rubber was scarce.
Manufacturers used synthetics.
Unreliable.
Fifteen dollars for a used bike.
Might as well have been a hundred.
With Daddy gone,
where would Mom get fifteen dollars?
Still, I hoped.

Enter Grannie.
Grannie sewed.
Sewed for the Rosedale ladies
who arrived at our house
in their long black cars,
their chauffeurs rushing to open doors.
Grannie never charged enough.
She, too, lived on the edge.
But, she managed a deal
with the second-hand store man.
Five dollars a month for two months
and a remodelling of his wife's old coat.

Queen Anne's Lace

Caroline H. Davidson

White lace nodding in the shade
like my grandmother's head
nodding as she cautions
"You can't be too careful,"
quoting Grandpa Henry.

She crochets white lace
rosettes clustered in circles
an antimacassar for the chair.
"Tell us about the salesman,"
we wiggle in anticipation
"the Bible Salesman."
She hooks a white thread
through and back
as she tells the tale.

"He knocked on my door
was ever so polite.
I asked him in, opened the parlour.
He said he was selling Bibles
and he looked so kind.
He had a small moustache,
hair combed back real nice,
a gentleman, but I suppose he'd have to be
selling Bibles.

"I would've offered him tea, but
your Grandpa Henry was there at the door,
big; he can carry two bales of hay.
"You best leave, now, Mister,"
rolling up his left sleeve with his right hand
hairs on his arm bristling.

"I said, "he's selling Bibles"
but Henry stepped forward.
The man stood up quick
no taller than Henry's shoulder
and real skinny.
His hair gleamed, I recall
smelled of macassar oil
like a real gentleman.

"I started to get up, but Henry's hand
was pressing on my shoulder.
"No call to come back here, Mister,
no call at all."

"After Henry went out to see him away
I picked up the antimacassar
from the back of the chair.
It smelled like your grandfather
when we were courting.
He used that hair oil at our wedding,
but not after.

"I like crocheting these doilies
sort of like flowers, that lace of Queen Anne
white by the roadside.
Makes me think of Henry
protecting me."

Reveries

Across Generations
For Karen
Kathryn MacDonald

Grandma's face, burnished and worn
like walnut, graces my memories.

You remind me of her
in your earthiness,
although you lack her grey-streaked bun
and crosshatched wrinkles.
Something about your eyes,
their intensity and feeling
burrowed deep
in pain never mentioned and joy.
You squat in your garden
fingers easing plants into soil.
Lilies and iris and leafy hosta
will reward your eyes with colour
(yellow, purple and pale-dawn blue).
Your honey-brown hair caught in a knot
strays free in a gust of spring breeze
as hers used to do.

Later you'll sit by the fire pit
legs wrapped in a quilt
sewn during snowy days
as forget-me-nots were sown today
(cloth pieced into squares,
patterns creating stories shared
from woman's heart and hand).

In her season she was like you
young and loving and loved.
By orange embers below night's sky
time collapses into sparks
across generations.

Old Granny in K~Town

for James Reaney and the late Tom Marshall

Michael Hurley

When Grandma was a girl
she wore whale-bone corsets
white gloves and petticoats
snug little bonnets
that tamed her hair
and broad-brimmed sun hats
that set it off
bringing the boys round
all the way from Gananoque.

Sitting bolt-upright in church
or parlour
prim and proper
or poised elegantly
(but not too lavishly)
beside bougainvillaea
at garden parties
in someone's honour
girl-grandma outran a growing shadow
painted on cobblestone
by gaslight,
and knew the names
of all the horses
up and down Ontario Street.

Yes and all the arches, domes and gateways
punctuating Edwardian Limestone City
like so many letters
from over home,
dear old England
her dear old heart
never stopped aching for
one whit, her ears deaf
to more modern things
never tired hearing about,
her silvery voice
never falling silent over,
not once, not ever.

When Grandma the woman
had children
(and many there were, too
not just me)
they grew up
and out of that sepia world
leaving her the sole survivor
of an invisible, unvisited kingdom
dwindling to the size
of a dollhouse
stuffed in an attic.

And when no one nowhere no longer
seemed to care
about such lost and mothballed worlds
withering away under the sea
of time
Grandma took to wrapping it
tighter round herself
like a decaying shawl
a curiosity of sorts
preserved intact
for decades
        eons!
intimate yet foreign
like a gallstone
inside a pickle jar,
a queen inside a coffin,
a grandma inside a poem
unread by those in pursuit
of more exciting fare.

Room in My Heart
Ruth Zaryski Jackson

Sadie turned the bell at the front door of my mother's rooming house on Charles Street and presented herself with a deep bow: "Hello, I'm Sadie Carlton. Have you a room to rent?" Just over five feet, she wore her finest navy pinstriped coat, a white handkerchief in the left breast pocket and white gloves. A smart fedora with a matching navy band covered her tight curls. Mother, in her grey housedress and apron, was dazzled. Sadie's rimless glasses highlighted bright blue eyes, which pierced my heart. I was smitten too. She moved in that afternoon and stayed for seven years.

Sadie was Irish but emigrated from Scotland in 1913. Pretty and stylish, she might have married the right man. Sadie's infectious laugh and lilting Scottish accent crept under my skin. Recalling it now, I am transported to that childhood time. She would urge me to cuddle up under a blanket in front of the big oil painting, and we'd make up adventure stories. Few props were needed to entertain. Tea parties for my dolls were staged around a wooden chest. We walked and ran in Queen's Park. She loved me unconditionally, and how I loved her!

In 1950, everything changed once we moved to the suburbs. Sadie did visit us but, by then, she was living with another family. She was no longer 'my' Sadie, and I didn't want to share her. Later, when she had cancer, she still came over, but her body smelled funny. It was a sour old lady smell – not the sweet comfy scent of a loving friend.

Years after her passing, I couldn't miss Sadie more if she'd been my real grandmother. Recently, I found her death notice in my desk and wondered if Sadie's family misses her as much as I do.

Granny's Garden

Ann Peacock

Granny's garden
Is alive
With colour

This spring day
I walk its paths
And think how much
She loves me
The smell of her flowers
Like a happy cloud
Around my head
I breathe deep

A bee moves everywhere
Making honey
For my toast
The sunlight and shadows
Call to me
I move forward
And climb the steps
Of her gazebo

A mist hangs
Over everything
I did not notice
Now it's all I see
It wraps itself around me
And lifts me to another world

In the distance
Granny waits
Her smile so warm
She calls my name
Her arms move to hug me

Granny, I say
I've come to take you home
Remember your garden
It's missing you
The flowers need your touch
Granny shows me her wings
She tells me she is happy
Someday I will join her
She says
Just before she disappears

The sun touches me
And I am back
On the garden pathway
Alone
I smile
I love my Granny's garden
In Spring
It holds memories

Passages

A Very Good Soul

John Pigeau

1

You died on a Saturday in June, shortly after sunrise. Mom and I were by your bedside, sleepily watching a CBC documentary on a family who'd adopted a deer as a household pet. The deer had befriended the family's cat. They were the best of mates, it was clear, the deer licking the cat till it couldn't possibly get any cleaner (or happier); the two of them frolicking in the snow; finally, both of them asleep, side by side, on a large mattress on the floor.

There was a beat of silence from the television, and I could not hear something I'd gotten used to hearing. I turned to look at you, under the thin green covers on the hospital bed, and your twisted mouth was open—as it had been for eight long days after your second stroke—but now I couldn't hear your steady, though laboured, breathing. I looked at Mom and leaned in closer. Your chest was not rising and falling.

You had gone.

2

Gram is asleep in the dark blue recliner next to her bed, which is freshly made. It's mid-afternoon, but Gram also looks polished for the day, in a light blue cashmere sweater and smart grey slacks, her pouchy cheeks a little rosy. I look at Erin and smile; Erin smiles back.

"Hi, Gram," I say, walking into the room. Gram smiles when she sees us, her hazel eyes gleaming. I always think she could be anywhere—in the bowels of a factory, on a gurney in the back of an ambulance, or here, at Pleasant View Nursing Home—and when she spotted a family member, she'd give the same pretty smile. It's the sort of smile that can cheer you up, make you feel thankful.

"Hi," Gram says, looking mostly at Erin. She loves Erin. Gram's only met her a half dozen times, but when we visit, Gram pays lots of attention to her as if she were already family.

"Hi," Erin says sunnily. "We brought you something."

"Oh."

I tell Gram, "Mom said not to bring you anything with too much sugar, but I know you love these." Erin hands her the lemon tarts.

"Oh," Gram says again, and I know by that she means 'thank you'. Sometimes, the words she wishes to speak just won't come. She surprises me and says, "Thanks."

I sit on the bed, Erin in the extra chair in Gram's small but nicely furnished room. There's a beautiful view out a very large window of a wooded area, where deer prance about and people take walks with the nursing home staff, volunteers, or family members. It's a sunny day, but Gram's looking at the lemon tarts.

"I'll open those for you," I tell Gram. "You want one now?"

"Yes."

"Maybe, just have one now and save the other one for later," I suggest. Gram is diabetic and has to watch the sweets, though she loves them so. Mom hounds me about the treats Erin and I bring her. "She's ninety-five," I tell her. "What harm can it do? If Gram passes away after eating a chocolate donut, Mom, she'll have died happy."

Mom clucks her tongue at that or says, "That's not the point." Mom is Gram's only daughter. Their bond is a strong one, comprehensible only to them. She would do anything to make Gram's life better. And she does, buying Gram ultra-comfortable blankets for her bed, the softest pillows, the warmest socks, the prettiest blouses, and taking her for trips to the countryside or to my sister's, so Gram can see her four great-grandchildren.

Gram eats a lemon tart, and I tell her about our new kitten, Benny. Erin chimes in. "He bites, he scratches, he plays hilariously," she says. Gram seems tickled.

But I know Gram will never meet Benny or see the wonderful new apartment Erin and I share in Westport (a second-floor abode; Gram could never get up all those stairs), and that makes me sad. I shake these thoughts away.

"How have you been feeling?" I ask Gram, and she nods and scrunches up her nose as if to say 'So-so'. She looks at Erin and then at me, and says, "I never thought I would live this long."

"I don't think anyone ever thinks they'll live to ninety-five, Gram," I say, quite honestly.

"No," Gram says thoughtfully. In her contemplative look, you can see she's thinking of all the days gone by – all those birthdays and Christmases, weddings and parties and funerals, jobs and bosses and friends come and gone. The eldest of seven children, all Gram's sisters and brothers have passed on.

My Great Uncle Jack (after whom I was named), Gram once lovingly and laughingly told me, was a rascal, a real weed. Smoked dandelion cigarettes and chased all the girls. He caught heck for it, too—Gram's father was a stern but kind man, I've gleaned—but that never stopped Jack from filching a flask of whisky or a few bucks off his father's night table. And there was Kaye, poor Kaye, who died quite young of a "weak heart"—and Frank, who succumbed to tuberculosis at the age of four. Then there was Marion, the family beauty, a voracious reader who once ran a bakery with her husband in Gravenhurst and lived her life by astrological charts. Gram's other sister, Dodi, wrote me letters all the time; they were clever and funny and filled with prayers for me, though I never did meet her. Finally, there was Ted, who fought in WWII and returned safe and sound from France to work at the post office.

Gram never spoke of Mom's father. We do not know his name, only that he was a Norwegian soldier. Gram had other worries through the years, like food and shelter and medical bills. In a time when it was uncommon to have a child out of wedlock, Gram did exactly that, and she raised Mom by herself, working at various department stores and photographers' studios to pay her bills. She never drove – walking or taking the bus wherever she needed to go – and thus her lifelong advice to me: "Always take good care of your feet."

To me, Gram is an amazing human being, smart and strong and courageous. When I think about her life – looking after her brothers and sisters as a child, raising a child of her own as a single mother, and the many days and nights of loneliness that must have followed Mom getting married and moving out – I really cannot fathom the depth of her fortitude. It seems larger than me. If I can be even half as dignified as she, half as strong, half as brave, I will consider myself a very good soul.

When our visit's over, Gram insists on walking us to the front doors. Using her walker, she easily keeps pace with Erin. I lag behind a bit, and watch Gram smile at everyone we pass in the hallway – a frail woman in a wheelchair, a busy nurse, a hunchbacked man sitting on a chair next to his oxygen tank. The chemical smell of this place unsettles my stomach. I wish we could kidnap Gram. Take her to Pizza Hut. Make up a beautiful room for her at our place, and watch black and white movies with her at night. I wonder who her favourite actor was. Charlie Chaplin? Cary Grant? And did her high school girlfriends ever give her a nickname? Who took her on her first date? I wonder if she was ever madly in love.

Near the front doors, Gram says, "Do you go this way?" and she gestures toward the circular driveway out front. I don't understand what she means; there's no exit where she's gesturing. But Erin tells her, "We can."

Gram blinks and seems pleased. "Good," she says.

We say our goodbyes. Outside, in a fresh spring breeze, Erin links arms with me as we walk toward her car. "She's such a sweetheart," she says.

"I know," I say and smile. Then: "Did she mean drive around the circle so she can wave goodbye to us?"

"Yes. I think so."

"That's so sweet," I say. I could cry from the joy this brings me. I hold Erin tighter and tell her I love her.

"I love you too," she says, squeezing my hand.

We drive around the circular driveway, and I roll down my window to better see Gram. There she is, by one of the large bay windows, standing with her walker, smiling and watching. I wave. Gram doesn't wave back – her hands are on her walker – but she's still smiling, as we drive toward the exit.

I do not know this is the last time I will see her smile.

Grandma Lebedow
Elynne Chaplik-Aleskow

She is one of the great loves of my life. I lost her in a plane crash February 12th, 1963, but the memory of my maternal grandmother Fannie Lebedow inspires me to this day.

I was my grandma's first grandchild. The bond between us was magical. One of my favourite treats as a little girl was sleeping over at her apartment. The room I slept in had twin beds that were so high and fluffy, I needed help getting in at night.

One morning, my grandma came to check on me, and I was not in bed. The window next to the bed was halfway open. She panicked, thinking that I had fallen out the window! Grandma was relieved to discover that I had fallen off the bed and in my sleep rolled underneath. Years later, we would share a good laugh about that morning's discovery.

My grandmother was a tall woman with striking silver hair. She was handsome and stately in her carriage with soft smooth skin that always smelled like fresh Palmolive soap. People would turn their heads to see her when she entered a room.

She was my grandma, a woman whose affection for me was unconditional and giving. Loving her was natural and easy, because she loved me back with such genuine joy and caring.

It always felt good to be around her. I looked forward to seeing her, touching her, and smelling her scent. With Grandma Lebedow, I shared many of the happiest moments of my childhood.

One of the greatest legacies my grandmother left me was showing me how to love. She passed this natural gift to my mother as well.

While my mother remembers her mother always stunningly attired, that is not the childhood memory of her that I cherish. I treasure a picture I have of Grandma in the housedress she wore to take me grocery shopping.

At the store, she would tell me to pick out any candy I wanted. I always got the pretzel stick. I would hold her hand as we walked, returning home in time for the delicious lunch she would prepare. Her kitchen pantry filled with desserts was like Disneyland to me.

As I grew older, my grandmother became a friend with whom I could share my feelings. When I was 12 years old, Mom and I had our worst argument. I packed my belongings, willed my precious board games to my sister Linda and ran away from home. Of course, I ran to my grandmother's new apartment, only a few miles from my house.

When I arrived, my grandmother fed me and waited until I was ready to talk. She never pressured me. To this day, her legacy of listening without judgment is one I continue to implement in my relationships.

A few years after losing my grandfather, my family convinced my grandmother to take a vacation in Florida. She was with my mother and youngest sister Ivy at the beginning of her holiday. Before they left for home, my mother found a small hotel for seniors, and my grandmother stayed on alone for twelve more days.

My beloved grandma never made it home. The commercial plane she was on hit a squall during the first ten minutes it was in the air and crashed in the Florida Everglades. Everyone on board was killed. My grandmother was sixty-seven.

I can still touch the raw agony of that day when we found out that we lost her. I was seventeen and about to graduate from high school and head to college in the fall.

We were assured her death was quick, but I will never really know if she had time to be afraid. That question tortures me when I allow myself to think about it.

To Americans, February 12th is Lincoln's birthday. For my family, that date marks a personal devastation from which we will never recover.

In losing Grandma Lebedow, I lost one of the great loves of my life. I hope she would be proud of the woman I have become. I smile at her picture every day. Frozen in time in her housedress, she smiles back at me.

Translating Grandma

K. V. Skene

Suddenly mummy was dead and there she was
in a just-pressed housedress, flowered
'pinafore'
'hoovering' the carpet,
finding 'plasters' for our skinny knees
and she already knew we hated 'swedes'. Of course
we were big enough to fetch 'reels of cotton' from
'Wollies',
drop in the 'ironmongers' for 'javelle water' or 'pop'
to the 'chemists' for 'lozenges' and,
dry the 'washing-up' or collect
the emptied 'dustbins'. See, here she is
in her Sunday best and Grandpa's pearls,
looking straight at Dad who's holding the camera.
Unsmiling …
Her teeth hurt.

Anticipated Visits

Carolyn R. Wilker

When I was twelve years old, Grandma and Grandpa W. bought a lot on the side road close to the home farm where we lived and where they had raised their children. The lot was graded and the foundation had been poured. I was looking forward to having my grandparents living close by. I wanted to spend more time with this grandmother I saw less often.

I must have been about seven or eight years old when I stayed overnight at their home in the city. Grandma understood about shadows in houses and left a nightlight on for me. Grandma gave me choices and made the foods I liked to eat, and after the concert in the park, she and Grandpa treated me to ice cream. Grandma really listened when I talked to her; those pale blue eyes, like my Dad's, rested gently on me. She showed me that I mattered, even if I was only a kid.

I remember one of the dresses Mom made for me from fabric Grandma brought back from Florida. There was enough cloth for two dresses, back in the days when Mom dressed my sister and me alike.

During my grandmother's last weeks, my parents told us, "Grandma's really sick; she's going to the hospital," and "the doctors are going to operate." I would have liked to comfort her, except that I was ill, too, though not nearly so sick as she. Being protected from hard truths, I never dreamed she wouldn't get better.

Grandma died during the operation. The cancer was advanced, and she was too weak to endure the trauma of surgery. All that was left to us kids was to prepare for her funeral and listen to the hushed tones of adult conversation and one-sided long distance calls to relatives.

Grandma lay there in her casket in her Sunday dress, hair curled and set. Her round, wire-rimmed glasses had been placed across the bridge of her nose where they normally sat, even if she didn't need them anymore. She would feel no more pain, my mother had said, as my Dad looked on, tears glistening in his eyes.

Grandma's funeral, on Valentine's Day that year, came in the middle of a winter storm. I was to stay at home, out of the cold wind that made me cough. The wind howled around the eaves like a pack of hungry wolves, increasing my sadness as I waited for my parents and sisters to come home. I tried to imagine the service that I was missing and remembered Mom saying that Grandma would be in heaven, a strange form of comfort even to a child who believed in God.

Grandpa didn't stay long in that house on the side road. Too many memories, I guess. I visited him wherever he went, even after he moved to Florida.

Our children have not known this set of grandparents, and I have missed sharing this part of my life with them. It's been a long wait, but on my next visit with my grandmother, I'll have so much to tell her.

Traces

From The Nursing Home Window

Janet L. Harvey

She wishes for the wash-out spring morn.
Tulips sprout their weary heads to the sunlight at last
She still smell coffee coming up the stairs
And feel the other side of her bed warm.
He is whistling as he shaves. Last time they made love –
He mentally touched her on the buttock
While they sip hot cocoa on the porch
She'd passed him for refill,
He winked in the dark, she didn't notice.
Yesterday he'd spent hours writing lyrics on her
Swivels belly and smooth legs, he curl his tongue
Around the words touching her earlobes.

Again. She'd be eighteen –
mad about the boy in the back seat
Later he'd wed her with aluminium foil ring
And pluck the stars, hang them on the plane to Paris
Her name Margarita hangs on his skull. Until it wears
The amber from his hair.
He showers her in roses – after he pick the thorns away.
From harsh word. He was never mad enough.
But she cries along with the baby,
who was scared of thunder.
Clapping on housetop.
Rain ripple the pond overflowing to her feet.

Even though she'd never painted her toes whore red
She thought of it though.
Yes, she thought of many things
Like wearing no undies around the house.
Chiffon dress
She'd paint the look in his eyes when he notice her.
Alluring He penetrate her from across the room –
And she will smile.
She will bloom in June many colours –

Sun yellow the day the doctor announce it's another boy.
Who will replace him one spring morning – between coffee
And cinnamon rolls he sang one last sang
The words ascend the stairs
And perfumed his side of the bed. In Grave silence.
The Virgin Mary preserved him there under the apple tree.

A place she wishes to be. But today this wheelchair.
A prison
From the nursing home window she lost in dream
Of the outside.
This rain-kissed spring morning
And tulips grow under the apple tree.

Babusia's Hands

Raïssa Chernushenko

Wizened and worn with work
seized at the joints by the chill
of picking sugar beets
daybreak to dusk

Tanned and spackled in fine white flour
pinching the filling into plump varenyky
lowered appallingly close to scalding bubbles

Removing uppers and lowers, both
toothbrush waving madly
grinning gummy smile – cackling witch-like
as we run shrieking in horrified glee

Splattered with primary colours
helping littler hands dip egg-laden spoons
into bowls of Easter dye
caressing shoulders in admiration

Hands catching hold of us
with fierce intensity that was – perhaps
love borne of fear – perhaps
of losses too innumerable to bear

Liver-spotted, with the sheen of stretched skin
opening stubborn jars of sauerkraut
borscht, pickles, jams
sure grip belying arthritic joints

Rubbing care into the bunions of feet
confined too long within the prison
of childhood shoes
the shoemaker's daughter

Unrolling bristly curlers
teasing tightly permed curls
into church hair
or catching into a net – stray pieces
misbehaving over the frying pan

Applying with practiced precision
the slick and chiselled remnant
of a 1950's scarlet red – still encased
in original silver tube

Hands held aloft in reverie – seldom joyous
fingers pointing blame – wagging grim reminder
that I should marry first
and always foremost for love

Soft doughy hands
clapping old country rhymes into song
bouncing on her lap – her first great grandchild
would that it were mine

Hands with scars and secret shames
etched into their lines
passed down until perhaps forgotten
but never quite gone

Hands last seen held clasped
across her breasts
unrecognizable to me as she
whispers in my ear
Don't let me go

My hands – now resembling hers –
setting the empty place
dusting the photos
that will always hold
her story

I keep the gift of measuring in pinches and palms
of attention to detail
and finding within the walls of my own chest
the courage to speak
and to love – until it hurts

Patterns

Louise O'Donnell

You left me no pattern, Grandmother,
to reconstruct the cobweb intricacies of your life.
I wanted to copy them into the pages of my days,
but you secreted them away
inside the drawers of your mind,
like the dimensions of the ladies who
brought you their dreams of filmy gowns,
of ruffles and feathers,
which you created with no printed patterns.

I searched for the soft shape of your youth,
but encountered only ragged swatches from distant
voices.
I wanted to know what pitfalls to avoid.

When did it all start to go wrong?
Was it the fire that burned down your farm?
Or was it the fire of your independence,
showing that with your needle
you could provide for yourself?
That needle bought you a house before women could vote,
fed you and your children.

I have daughters and granddaughters
who have inherited your fire.
What pattern to leave them?
I look at you now, from my own grandmother eyes,
know at last,
that the pattern they fashion
will be their own.

The Golden Years

Janet L. Harvey

Two old women torn by country and culture
Share the same room, a solid wall between their beds.
They sing the same songs,
Listen to the same piano player
On Mondays, on the second floor.

They smile at the nurses.
The blue skies may be grey, they aren't complaining.
They meet at the doorway, compare new wrinkles
Talk of yesterdays, count down the hours till morrow.

Dinner is always five, snack is always seven,
Bedtime between eight and nine-thirty.
They sleep until it's time for a change.
A nurse will roll them open –
Out of those wet diapers, twice a child.

In their sleep they lean on each other's past for strength.
The virgin freshness of youth smiles from memory boxes
Maintained on the wall at each door.
A single crochet rose
Tells that fingers were straight and without arthritis.
 It tells that they both loved Victorian corsets and bone china.
And by universal law, they are sisters – love the same man.

Tomorrow the sun rises in the east
Squeezes its nose through cracks of heavy drapes
Across their sleeping bodies. Again.

The hairdresser waits for them to swallow their toast
And scrambled eggs
Today they'll be stars with their white perms
And painted nails.

The bibs they wore at breakfast will be gone.
One will never know. They wear dancing shoes,
In 1906, on an evening laden with stars.

Now hips and metallic pins
Cause movements to be slow.
They smile at the nurses, knowing
One day someone will lay lilies at their feet.
When they'll join the others in the arms of mother earth
When lung clasps its last breath, they'll dance on angels'
wings
Leaving a feathered path in the clouds.

For an Old Woman
Who Carried On

K. V. Skene

who got up every morning, grey braid swinging,
rose flannel robe snugged, eyes hiding
behind smudged bifocals

and cooked porridge to 'stick to the ribs'
of her motherless children, all wrapped up
in hand-knit scarves and mittens

for the slow trudge to school from a house
she would not have chosen. Old woman
who measured time by our birthdays

whose hands turned small socks, squared
rounded shoulders,
your ghost still comes back as love.

Children

Learning to Lie

Laurie Lewis

I was six years old when I learned how to lie. My brother Andy taught me, but I don't think he knew he was doing it. We always fought with each other, so he wouldn't ever deliberately teach me anything. But I knew he told silent lies – testing the wrath of God to see if there was a lightning bolt out there ready to flatten a kid who was just trying to keep out of trouble. That was a time before the lies became necessary. He was almost eight years old.

We had just come from Calgary, and my mother was trying to find a job in Vancouver. My father was in Prince Rupert looking for work – that's what my mother told us to say. Andy and I had been plunked with our father's parents on their farm near White Rock. It was the middle of the Depression, although we didn't know that then, in 1936.

In the mornings, my grandfather drove to his carpentry job. On the way, he delivered cans of milk to the dairy pick-up station and dropped us off at school. After school, Andy and I always walked home along the trail between the fields and the woods – three miles along the dark overgrown pathway – where Andy tormented me with stories that a wild bull was loose in the area (that wasn't really a lie), and I looked for raging beasts lurking behind every shrub.

My grandmother was always up early to milk the eight cows. The cans from the previous evening's milking had cooled all night in a deep tank of water. The metal cans, heavy with milk, rested in the waterhole next to the barn, in a deep wet space that I found terrifying. Whenever I had to go through the cooler shed, I pushed myself back against the wall, far away from the dark hole. I was afraid of falling in, but felt drawn to the edge. The hole seemed to murmur frightening things, and I thought there might be a person deep down in the well. I knew what the hole would do to a person, how you would never get out, but spend your whole life wetly in the echoing dark.

My grandmother Charlotte packed lunches for us to take to school, jam sandwiches, the same kind she had made for each of her own ten children. Twenty years of jam sandwiches, the red jam staining slabs of white bread. All the farm wives made the same kind of bread, using mostly the same recipes, baked in the same big black cook stoves. It was honest homey bread. My grandmother cut thick slices for breakfast, lunches, and tea.

Every school day, she wrapped the sandwiches neatly in waxed paper, with a double fold on top to seal them, and triangles like tent flaps at the ends. She put the two sandwiches in a brown paper bag, soft from re-use, and handed it to Andy.

"Now you take care of your sister at lunch and give her a sandwich, you hear me?"

We rode in the back seat of the car; it was a 1929 Durant, and the front seat next to the driver had been taken out to make room for four 10-gallon cans of milk. Our grandfather drove to the highway intersection where a wooden platform had been constructed as a pick-up spot for the local dairy. On the way there, the full cans thudded heavily against each other in the car, the metallic sound muffled by the rich milk inside. When he lifted them onto the platform, he grunted at the weight. The empties from yesterday, he lifted easily into the car. The lids were off and dangled noisily against the side of the cans, fastened to the handles with a short chain. The cans rattled and clanged against each other as the car turned toward the school at last.

Here, in the countryside at White Rock, everything was strange and different, scarier to me than the apartment near Calgary's Chinatown where we had been living before my father went away. The schoolhouse was set into an acre of yard, with two neat rows of outhouses at the back and a large open shed to hold the winter's supply of firewood. Four or five swings dangled from wooden frames. Trees and shrubs edged the clearing. The children in the schoolyard all knew each other, had known each other for years. It was my first year at school and I was shy and frightened. I missed my mother.

Inside the school, there was just one big room with four rows of desks. Students of all grades were there, up to grade eight. The teacher walked up one aisle and down the other, looking at what everyone was doing. I sat in the first seat of the first row. In the seat behind me sat the one other first grader – Milton. The kids called him Milkweed.

Whenever I finished my work, I had to teach Milton. He wasn't as scared as I was in first grade, because he had been there the previous year, too. I loved learning things and helping Milton. I just listened and watched and tried not to get noticed, looking at Milton working with his yellow pencil. When I finished with him, I could listen to the lessons for the other grades: reading, arithmetic, history. I especially liked it when the teacher or one of the big kids read stories and poems out loud. They recited things like "I wandered lonely as a cloud …"

On the day I learned to lie, as we left the car in the morning Andy was daydreaming as usual – that's what they always said: I suppose he was daydreaming as usual – and the brown lunch bag was left on the back seat. At the noon recess, Andy told me: No sandwiches, No lunch. "And don't cry, you little twerp. And don't tell anyone."

I sat on the big grey steps of the school, exactly halfway up and halfway down, right next to the railing, and reached my hand up to hold it for comfort.

At lunchtime, I usually took my sandwich and sat in a green cave under the bushes, but I was afraid to go in there when I had no lunch. I knew that children were starving in China, and I wondered how long it would take me to starve to death. I didn't think I would die before teatime, anyway, but perhaps I would lapse into a coma. That was something I had heard from my mother once in Calgary, just before her father died, "He lapsed into a coma."

The teacher came down the steps. She always ate her lunch in the school room – where she could have some peace and quiet, she said – and then she usually went for a little walk.

"Have you finished lunch already?"

"No, Miss Harris," I said, not even thinking about telling a lie.

"Well, don't you think you should eat it instead of dawdling here on the steps?"

A raspy lump formed in my throat, and I could feel my chin quivering. How could I not tell the truth? How could I not cry? So I had to tell. Oh, I knew Andy would be so angry.

"Well, I'll see what I can do. Go and find your brother, please. He must be hungry, too."

She walked down the road and around the corner to the house by the river. When she came back, she had two sandwiches wrapped in waxed paper, just the way my grandmother did it, with the little foldover and the tent flaps. They were jam sandwiches, too, red jam like Gramma's, and tasted delicious.

But I was shocked. Jam and butter. There was butter on that sandwich! Even at six years old, I knew what a "cash crop" was. My grandparents got paid money for these things, so they were precious. Apples were a cash crop, except the scabby ones, which we ate. Eggs were a cash crop; that's why Andy and I had half a fried egg each at supper, and my grandfather had a whole one. So was milk – and butter. We never wasted butter on sandwiches.

After school, when we started to walk home, Andy was very angry.

"You're a dope. You know that? You had to go and tell, didn't you?"

My throat got raspy again and tears tried to get out.

"Get away from me," he told me. "You walk home alone. Go on."

"It's not fair. You ate your sandwich, too. And anyway, it's not my fault. Miss Harris made me tell."

"You're not supposed to tell things. Don't you know anything? Dummy."

He made me walk all the way alone, far in front of him along the trail, under the big trees, in the dark wet shadows where the wild things were. I looked behind me to see if he was there, but I saw only shadows. Andy usually walked ahead of me, calling back, "Hurry up, you twerp. Come on, step on it." I'd call out to him, "Wait for me, Andy, wait for me." And I would try to run fast to catch up with him. But that day I couldn't see him at all; I looked far far ahead for the brightening that would tell me the road was near. Soon, soon, please let it be there.

When I reached home, my grandmother met me in the lane. She had found the lunch bag in the car when Granddad got home from work. "I was so worried," she said. "What did you do for lunch? And where's Andy?"

I started talking right away. I told her all about the children starving in China and about being rescued by Miss Harris, and the jam sandwich from the lady by the river.

"Did you have enough to eat?" she asked. "Was it a good sandwich?" She worried about everything. I saw her thin old face and raggedy hair bending over me. But suddenly my mouth just stopped.

I didn't tell about the butter. About the cash crop.

"Sure, Gramma, it was nice," I told her. And I hugged her around her apron.

Andy came up the lane then, turning in from the road. He stood right next to me, silent and watching, waiting for trouble. He was used to being in trouble though, so maybe he didn't mind too much. He just stood there, looking at me.

All of a sudden, I decided not to tell about him making me walk home alone. He hadn't told me not to tell on him, but I knew. I didn't tell about being alone and scared, about walking the dark trail by myself.

"It was a good sandwich, Gramma, but not as good as yours," I told her. And my grandmother smiled at me just like a little girl.

Once I learned, I got really good at not telling. That year when I was six, I discovered a power in knowing something secret; a way of having thoughts when nobody knows. And in that space of "not-telling", I found a person that might be me. Sometimes the thoughts I stored up were as simple and smooth as butter, sometimes as frightening as the wild things in the woods. Or dark and wet as the waterhole into which my grandmother would one day lower herself in despair, wearing her winter coat to keep out the cold.

Now I'm a grandmother myself, and life has become smoother and easier. I use my pension to buy just the kind of bread I like – a sourdough from a good bakery in Kingston. I put butter on my morning toast, and strawberry jam, too. And I sit munching meditatively by my window, watching the neighbourhood children on their way to school, perhaps watching for someone like Andy – someone like me.

Grandma's House

Judith Cleland

Every kid should have a Grandma's house.
Halfway between his house and school is best.
And there should be a grandma always there
For times when he's been teased or failed a test.

Inside the house there has to be a chair.
A chair that's big, with room enough for two,
Where Grandma sits all afternoon alone
And wishes someone would stop by – like you.

You walk up to the door and knock politely
Then open it and call "Grandma, it's me."
She jumps up from her chair, fixing her hair
And straightening her clothes, she comes to see

If she could be so lucky as to have
A grandchild who is clever and gets stars
On papers that he's written about rain
Or won a race or lost a fight or worse.

To Grandma it's no matter what you've done,
Spilled your father's coffee in the car,
Whether you have freckles or chew gum
Or waste your daytime dreaming on a star.

She hurries to the door to greet you, saying
"The kettle's warm – let's go and make some tea.
Where have you been? I've missed you so, my child."
Every kid should have a grandma just like me.

Martha McKay Brown
1875–1947

Kathleen M. Martin

1

Martha McKay Brown, my Scottish maternal grandmother and the only grandparent I knew, died three weeks after my last visit with her, just before my eleventh birthday. I had lost the chance to say 'Sorry', and this became more immediate and troubling to me than her death.

My strong attachment to this matriarch began when my granny became my primary caregiver, along with my spinster aunt Jessie. After spending months as an infant convalescing in a hospital, I was taken by my grandmother forty miles away from the tenements, the factories, the noise and smoke-filled atmosphere of the big city.

Putting colour in my pale cheeks and fattening me up with good food and a daily dose of cod liver oil would be her mission. She was determined that I would thrive on fresh, clean air in the small, pastoral and slow-paced town of Crieff. Granny's plan also helped my mother to have the bed rest she needed to deliver a healthy second child. Most of my extended visits continued until after the birth of my brother, and again when my sister arrived two and a half years later.

Life became hard for my granny, when at age thirty-two, her first husband died, leaving her with five children: three boys and two girls. By age forty-five, she was widowed again, leaving her with four more children. My mother being the eldest of these four, at only ten years old, was broken-hearted when her father died.

2

In order to make ends meet, Granny would walk to work before daylight. Her jobs were lighting the fires, preparing the breakfasts, and doing chores for families who lived in the mansions on the hilly part of town.

Those siblings still in school helped with the younger ones until Granny returned, usually carrying a basket of dirty clothes to be laundered and ironed. Older brothers still living at home left early in the morning for work within the region, while the eldest son laboured and lived on a farm, sending his money home. Two older sisters moved to St. Andrews, and worked as live-in nannies.

I believe I inherited a strong sense of family from my granny, for there was a role for each child within this blended family, where the term 'half brother or half sister' was never used. Naturally, sibling rivalry occurred, especially when the eldest brother would try to be the father and take on a strict, heavy load. But, with Granny's strong character, and her knack for knowing what was best for her children, she sent Alex off to sea to a programme for strong-willed young boys. Two years later, Alex was enlisted for the First World War and returned at the end of the war highly decorated.

As the firstborn granddaughter, I was the one to spend the most time with Granny and to be given her first name 'Martha' as my middle name, which made me feel special, even though, during my primary school-age years there were times I didn't like it. Granny, on the other hand, portrayed its biblical meaning as "Keeper of the House."

In my earliest memory, I fell off a swing and the bolt on the swing hit the corner of my eye, causing blood to stream down my cheek. Granny, dressed in her long black coat, and wide-brimmed black hat, held by a hatpin the size of a long, fine needle, pressed a towel to my face as she cuddled me in the backseat of a neighbour's car. I left the hospital like a war hero, with a bandage covering my head and a scar shaped like an anchor.

3

When I turned eight years old, I spent most of my seven weeks of summer holidays at Granny's house. I'd make the journey to visit her by myself. My mum would see me off at the bus station, and Jessie would meet me at the end of my trip. I looked forward to these visits with Granny, for I knew I could count on a haven of calmness and predictability in my surroundings, rather than the daily tension and displeasure voiced by my father.

Granny, although good to me, had a firmness blended with kindness. Her expectations of me grew as she aged and became a diabetic. I helped by making my bed, dusting the dresser, washing dishes, setting the table, ironing hankies and pillow slips and going for the messages. Granny believed 'idle hands are the devil's play', a phrase repeated many a time. I could not go out to play with my younger cousins or Morag, the friend who lived nearby, until the visiting nurse had given Granny her daily insulin injection.

My grandmother instilled giving, sharing, taking responsibility and honesty. These traits were set by example through her commitment to family. I never heard the word 'love' in her conversations with me or any family member, only in her hymn singing. We all knew that Jesus loved us, for Granny sang it loud and clear at Salvation Army meetings.

On cool summer evenings, after I got changed into my cosy nightgown, Granny, Jessie and I sat by the fireside listening to the radio, playing dominoes, looking at pictures of bygone days, or writing letters and postcards to my mum and dad announcing my safe arrival or my expected return date.

Each night at bedtime, she carried the oil lamp up the darkened hallway as she escorted me to the bedroom. She tucked me in bed, and then offered me the red box of promises, which was filled with biblical phrases printed on furled, beige paper. I held the small pincers and hovered over the box, deciding which tiny scroll to pluck from it. I unfurled the paper and read the message to Granny, and she took her turn and read her promise to me.

4

My main job, since Granny's health declined, was to go uptown for the messages. I learned weights and measures at the butcher and the greengrocer by reading the scales. I became proficient at mental arithmetic and the counting of pounds, shillings, and pence. I'd compare my costs to the shop assistant's calculations as she itemized each purchase, one by one, on paper. These skills earned me the title of 'good shopper' by Granny, for I always came back with change.

I learned a lot of life's practical and worthwhile lessons from my grandmother. I learned family values; fair work ethics; handling of life's disappointments; bringing my wants to my means; being generous; being content and honest; and never holding a grudge. It is this last lesson, which at the time of her death, I had not yet mastered, and for which I felt guilty.

I recall it clearly, coming in teary-eyed, bemoaning some unfair treatment by Morag towards me. Granny became annoyed at my trifling tale and admonished me in a tone I hadn't heard before.

"She could buy ye at one end of the street and sell ye at the other," she said.

Although, I didn't understand the full meaning of this statement, I did understand, at that precise moment, the sun, the moon and the stars were not shining in my favour.

Jessie suggested maybe it was time I went home, explaining that Granny wasn't too well. I also sensed it was time to leave. Two days later, I got ready to go home, feeling hurt and confused.

I can see Granny dressed in her dull paisley apron, which covered her black skirt and her black cardigan, pulled tightly over her large bosom. Her long grey hair, knotted in a bun at the back of her head, was held in place with large hairpins.

5

She shuffled towards me in her orthopaedic shoes while tapping her way across the linoleum floor with her cane. "Tak care, lass. Send a postcard when ye arrive." Her hug lasted long enough for me to inhale the smell of Lily of the Valley talcum powder.

"Watch yer time, or ye'll miss yer bus," she said.

"Cheerio, Granny," I said.

When I picked up my suitcase, Granny turned to take her usual pose by the large picture window. As I reached the large oak tree, I turned with a final wave, knowing she'd be there offering her feeble wave back before I rounded the corner in the pathway. For the first time, I didn't cry on the bus on the way back home. I, too, had turned a corner.

Many years later, and a grandmother myself, I travelled from my home in Canada back to Scotland to visit Granny's gravesite. Jessie, now in her late sixties, had become extremely hunched. Her gait was slow as she led the way through the stoned pathways of the cemetery. I followed a few steps behind, our crunching footsteps breaking the silence in this old part of the cemetery cradled in the valley. Occasionally, we stopped to read poetic and loving inscriptions on headstones.

"Just up here a wee bit," Jessie said. She looked puzzled, peering to read a few stones.

"Right here," she said, pointing to a patch of grass.

"Where's Granny's headstone?" I asked.

"Oh, she never had one," Jessie said. "I know she is next to this stone marked 'Robertson'."

I wasn't prepared for this news. How sad I thought, knowing Granny's resting place needed cues from another's headstone before we could pay honour to her memory. I felt affronted on behalf of my grandmother. How would the world know she lived, and how would anyone know her devotion to her family of nine children and twelve grandchildren?

6

Before I left to come back to Canada, Jessie and I selected and paid for a headstone. The inscription below Granny's name had space for an inscription for Jessie. Lot 64 in the old cemetery would become her resting place beside her mother.

Six months later, Jessie sent me photographs of the black marble headstone, erected in loving memory of "Martha McKay Brown".

Skoochimaru

Anne Watson-Russell

Against my opinion, she came into my life – will-he, nil-she. What chance, this child of children, this accident of blame and shame?

She got me, Day One. She calmly looked up at me from the pouch of my arms, our eyes locked, and I saw in her the generations – my children, my mother, my father, me. What she saw was love; unconditional love at first sight. And love is all she sees when she looks at me, even now. I am lost in her spirit, her fun, her promise. I am her grandmother – hers forever.

The difference between being a grandmother and a mother lies in knowing how short a time we have together. I am acutely aware that any delightful stage in her development will soon give way to another, equally delightful – but the first will be gone. To savour her ages and stages, that is my pleasure. Deadlines, appointments, schedules all fall away when Skoochi comes over to paint pictures, bake muffins, clap hands and dance. My hours with her are but seconds in the scheme of her life; fleeting, precious seconds.

Too busy setting up a career and a home – I missed so much of my own children's lives. She is giving me back what I squandered.

And her parents, how are they doing? They're growing up, of course – establishing their own careers and a home. How grateful I am they were still rebels when they were expecting her. Imagine a world without Skoochi in it? Unthinkable!

Ottawa Valley Lascaux
Patricia Anne Elford

In one of the one and one-half storey wartime houses that stood like soldiers on both sides of a field-ended street, lived my mother, my father, my brother and myself.

My mother used the wringer washer on Mondays, ironed on Tuesdays, shopped on Wednesdays, scrubbed on Thursdays – just like the embroidery on my handkerchief set said mothers did. I no longer use cloth handkerchiefs, and I can't remember what she did on Fridays. Every day of Dad's working life, Mom did household chores all morning and had a nap and a bath late in the afternoon, changing to a fresh housedress to welcome him home. Almost every night of Dad's working life, I fell asleep to the strum of my mother's treadle sewing machine.

On Saturday mornings, Mom baked. The family all walked to the library in the afternoon and played cards or games at night. On Sundays, we walked together to church.

Meals were on time. There was only one correct route for my brother and myself to walk to school. We had chores and were expected to obey both parents. Though my mother was intelligent and articulate, and though she encouraged all kinds of creative endeavours on our part, there was little indication for my brother and me of her "break-the-rules" side.

Perhaps my only hint came when, one day, to demonstrate something to my teenaged self, she threw down the oven mitts, crossed her arms with her hands down on her knees, and right between the wood-and-coal stove and the green-checkered tablecloth, showed me how to do the Charleston. My mother – a flapper? In a moment, it was over.

My mother liked neatness and stability. Over the years, the furniture was kept in the same positions. The house, when repainted, tended to have the same shades of green, inside and out. The ceilings were regularly cleaned with a broom wrapped in cloth. The walls were painted each spring. Nothing was to be tacked on them. My brother and I had bedroom bulletin boards for that purpose.

One special weekend many years later, my husband and I brought our children back to my small former home for a visit. The neighbouring houses, despite years of having been scraped and painted, with occasional attempts at asbestos siding, had been peeling regularly. An aluminum siding company had smelled opportunity. One after another, the houses were wearing new overcoats.

We exchanged the usual greetings at the door with Grandma where, upon crowding into the old house, we headed straight to the cookie jars, knowing our homemade favourites were hidden there. My mother, watching as this ritual was completed, appeared to have something on her mind.

Apparently, having this visit from her grandchildren had pushed her "rule-breaker" button. Giving the oldest child a box of 24 crayons and some coloured pencils, she told them all to go outside to draw and write on the outside walls of the house!

The children stood still, wondering if they'd been teleported to another dimension, and gaped at her. "Go ahead," Grandma urged, "Tomorrow, the aluminum siding goes on. What you write and draw will be there, under the siding, as long as this house is here. It will be your secret art gallery."

Hesitantly at first, then with laughter and shoving (no matter how big the wall, doesn't every child want the same place?), they built up stories and pictures. The children decorated Grandma's wall until they were exhausted.

Years later, after my mother had died, the house was sold. It still stands, keeping its secret about that wonderful day when, granted license by their grandmother, the children did just what children (including a much younger grandma?) have always wanted to do with pristine walls – they claimed them as their own.

Biography of the Editor:

Bonita Summers

Bonita Summers has recently left her position as an administrator of Queen's University to pursue the dual careers of writer and Therapeutic Touch™ practitioner. She is the author of *Woman with the Flying Mind*, an autobiographical collection of poems, the sales of which raised $1000 for Kingston Interval House, a refuge for abused women and children in Kingston, Ontario. Her book has also sold at such juried exhibits as Kingston's Fanfayr and the Kingston Women's Art Festival, due to Bonita's original photography, layout, and book design.

Bonita helped to organize Kingston's first dub poetry festival, Reloading the Can(n)on in November of 2006. Subsequently, she was invited to Toronto in May of 2007 to participate in the Dub Poetry Series put on by the Dub Poets' Collective.

Bonita's poem, *Electronic Junkie*, was published in *'Scapes*, an anthology of poems compiled from submissions by members of Kingston's Poetry & Company in 2007. Bonita was the administrator of Poetry & Company, a venue for established and emerging Kingston-area poets, for 2007.

In the same year, Bonita's poem, *Ode to Nan Yeomans*, was printed as a limited edition on an 1890's letterpress by Hugh Barclay of Thee Hellbox Press as a memento for contributors to Nan's Legacy – an endowment for aspiring artists with the Community Foundation.

Bonita's previous publishing credits include child raising articles for *Compleat Mother* and *Priority Parenting* magazines, a research piece on home birth and an exposé on federal government nuclear waste disposal tactics for *This Magazine*, a regular column on current events for Hornepayne's *The Bear News*, and Northern Ontario community coverage as a correspondent for *The Chronicle-Journal/Times-News* of Thunder Bay, Ontario.

Bonita's poem, *Belly Love*, is awaiting publication in an upcoming Canadian Federation of Poets anthology on childbirth. Currently, she is preparing her next book, *Digging Up the Bones*, for Hidden Brook Press' North Shore Series, and in the quiet hours of the night, working on a novel. Bonita also holds workshops on meditation, the chakra system, energy healing practices, intuitive writing, and poetry for catharsis and self-discovery.

Author Biographies:

Winona Baker

Winona Baker has written six books: *Not So Scarlet a Woman* and *Clouds Empty Themselves* were recommended for adult literacy courses by ABPBC; *Moss-hung Trees* received a Romanian medal; *Beyond the Lighthouse* was in Michael Budeja's *Read* and recommended *Writer's Digest* article (1994); her latest books are *Even a Stone Breathes* and *The Slough*.

Baker was International Prizewinner of The Foreign Minister's Prize celebrating Basho 1989. She has won tanka, humour, free verse, and sonnet contests; has poems in over 80 anthologies in North America, New Zealand, Japan and Europe; and been translated into Japanese, Croatian, French, Greek, Yugoslavian and Romanian.

It is said that her grandmother was the first woman graduate from a college now called the University of Prince Edward Island.

Elynne Chaplik-Aleskow

Elynne Chaplik-Aleskow, Distinguished Professor Emeritus of Wright College in Chicago, Illinois, U.S.A. and Founding General Manager of WYCC-TV/PBS, is an author, public speaker, and award-winning educator and broadcaster. Elynne is Chicago's first female television general manager.

Elynne's story *The Revolving Door* was published in *Chicken Soup for the Chocolate Lover's Soul*. Her essays and non-fiction stories have appeared in the *Chicago Sun-Times* and *Tribune*, *Innovation Abstracts Journal*, and magazines, including *Chicago Suburban Woman*, *Suburban Woman Northshore*, *The Rambler*, *Newcity*, *Releasing Times*, *ESL*, *The Heartlands*, *Sasee* and several online magazines, including the *Communication Research and Theory Network of the National Communication Association*, the *Blog Herald*, *Café She Ezine*, *Soap Opera Digest* website, *Pyschologies Magazine* website, *Moondance*, *Bread 'n Molasses*, and *TeachersCount* website. Her work will appear in three future print anthologies.

Elynne is married to her best friend, Richard Noel Aleskow. She considers being Fannie Lebedow's first grandchild among her greatest blessings.

Raïssa Chernushenko

After escaping the Ukraine during World War II, and spending several years in an Austrian refugee camp, Raïssa's paternal grandmother, Anna, came to Canada with her husband and two children on a work contract with an Alberta beet farmer. In the mid-1950's, she left her first husband, and made Toronto home for the last four decades of her life, during which time she remarried. Passionate about her grandchildren, she never failed to remind them to wear boots in the winter. How remarkable that this anthology coincides with the tenth anniversary of her passing.

Raïssa Chernushenko is trained in theatre, dance, psychodrama, and shiatsu therapy, and nurtures a lifelong love of travel. She currently resides in Oshawa, Ontario with her husband and two children. Previously published in professional newsletters and health magazines, she recently received an honourable mention in the first ever Writer's Circle of Durham Region Idol Contest.

Theodore Christou

Theodore Christou is a published poet and Ph.D. candidate in Queen's University's Faculty of Education. His research interests concern intellectual and conceptual history. He is examining the reception and interpretation of progressive education in Ontario during the interwar period.

Theodore spent his early years in Cyprus, where his extended family played a formative role in his development. The memories Theodore holds are sensual; these include the smell of jasmine and local herbs, the all-enveloping and arid heat, and the taste of organic foods unpolluted by centuries of foreign rule and occupation.

These memories, meeting in the visage of Theodore's grandmother, Pantelitsa, provoke deep nostalgia and heavy sadness. *Love, Sacred* honours his late grandmother who is, in many respects, representative of his native land. Frail and sad, ancient and strong-willed, she was Theodore's bridge to a heritage and to relations he lost when his immediate family moved to Canada, oceans and languages apart from his childhood home.

Judith Cleland

Judith grew up in Waterloo in close proximity to her maternal grandmother, whose family members were Mennonites from Pennsylvania. Grandma's house was home to many aunts, and there, life revolved around the garden and the kitchen. It was here Judith acquired her delight in all things natural and her true affection for the wisdom of female elders.

The fond memories of childhood in this milieu are the driving force in much of Judith's writing. *Voice of a Brown Bird* is her most recent collection of poems.

Karen L. Cole

Karen L. Cole is a retired English and drama teacher whose career spanned three decades and three countries. Karen's memoir of her life in the convent, *Lifting the Veil*, is awaiting publication. She is currently writing a novel based on her years in Jamaica. Karen has also published a number of articles on topics ranging from gardening to literature, two of her favourite pastimes.

Karen's maternal grandmother, Lena Ressler Rodewald, was born in Tower, Minnesota in 1889, but spent most of her life in the village of Spring Valley, Wisconsin. She was the mother of six children and numerous grandchildren and great-grandchildren. At the time of her death in 1986 at the age of 97, her descendants numbered fifty-eight. Her quilts and quirks were too numerous to count.

Karen lives in Whitby, Ontario with her husband and golden retriever.

Ellen Curry

Ellen was born and educated in Central Africa. She started volunteering at age 16 with First Aid for Red Cross. Ellen immigrated to Canada in 1961. She was a stay-at-home mom and volunteer at the school library where she was hired on as the school secretary. Ellen worked at the school for ten years and volunteered at her church.

Ellen became the owner/operator of Innerspace Dive Store. She set a Guinness World Record for staying underwater with scuba gear for 68 hours. Ellen retired in 1987 and took up golf, though continuing to work as a volunteer with special needs children.

Married for 52 years, Ellen and her husband have 2 sons and a daughter, 7 grandchildren, and 3 great-grandchildren. Ellen has published two children's books, a number of short stories in magazines, newspapers, and anthologies, and a booklet on aging. Her grandmother still walks beside her.

Caroline H. Davidson

Caroline H. Davidson has been living and daydreaming story plots and poetry lines for more than half a century. In 2004, she moved from Ontario to Ladysmith, B.C., bringing with her many mementos of life in her family home where her maternal grandparents had lived upstairs.

As a Methodist minister's wife, her grandmother was duty-oriented, but Caroline sensed a little regret when, at age 70, her grandmother said that she thought she would have liked dancing. From her, Caroline learned how to embroider and how to hold it together when there was chaos all around – a good lesson.

Caroline's poems have appeared in *Uncivilizing* by Insomniac Press, Toronto 1997, *Little Flowers*, a self-published chapbook in 2001, and in several anthologies of The Canadian Poetry Association and The Ontario Poetry Society. Caroline's life is full of music, writing, and friends.

J. Graham Ducker

Mr. Ducker is an honours graduate of Laurentian University in Sudbury, Ontario. Between 1971 and 1991, he was the principal, kindergarten teacher, and primary methods specialist at Morson Public School in Northwestern Ontario. His book of memoirs, *Don't Wake the Teacher!*, received a 9 out of 10 rating by www.BookIdeas.com.

His latest publication is a book of poetry, *Observations of Heart and Mind.*

Mr. Ducker has had many poems and short stories published in Canadian and international magazines. His most recent credit won first prize in the Lichen Arts and Letters Preview 'Writing Between The Lines' Contest. Mr. Ducker has had two recent honourable mentions in Writer's Digest contests.

As a member of the Canada Cuba Literary Alliance, Mr. Ducker recently spent two weeks in Cuba where he participated in readings at the University of Havana and the Havana Library and met with Her Excellency Ambassador Alexandra Bugailiskis.

Patricia Anne Elford

Patricia Anne Elford is a clergy person, educator, facilitator, editor and freelance writer who has been published in various genres: short stories, articles, poetry, youth materials, worship services, sermons, newsletters, book reviews, monologues and devotionals. She has been chosen to read her poetry at the Ottawa National Library and in other venues, having won standing and awards in several areas.

A professional member of The Word Guild (a national Canadian organization for writers who are Christians), Patricia taught a *Creativity* workshop at its latest national conference: Write!Canada 2007.

As indicated in *I Want My Grandma!*, Patricia has been bereft of grandparents since she was three, but her husband, adult children, grandchildren, and cats enrich her life.

Janet L. Harvey

Janet. L. Harvey lives in Thornhill, Ontario, Canada. She has had numerous poems published in a variety of Canadian and US magazines and international anthologies, including: *Sterling Silver*, *Feminine Magazine*, *Word Dance*, *Stella Showcase Journal*, *Spirit of Humanity* (Artists for a Better World), *Night Whispers* (Old Mountain Press), *Borderless Skies* (CCLA), and *Cross Culture* (Black Mail Press). Janet is Poetry Canada's Global Contest Winner.

Janet's poems in this anthology are a tribute to all the grandmothers she nurtures and cares for on a daily basis. These golden girls hail from different parts of the world and many cultures. They live as one in a community filled with love and compassion. They are treated with the utmost respect and dignity until it's time for them to cross over and join their loved ones.

Michael Hurley

According to Michael Hurley, only God knows what inspired the *Grandma Nuthin* piece, though if pressed by Zen toughs he'd have to say the *lila* of rascal saint Neem Karoli Baba, especially with Krishna Das and Ram Dass—the latter two of his favourite beings of all time, the former of all timelessness. (And, of course, kudos to wise guy Wes Nisker.)

Michael teaches poetry to the army, navy, and air force at the Royal Military College, Kingston, Ontario, and figures like the one in *Old Granny in K-Town* keep popping up throughout Canlit. *Grandmother Moon* is written not *in* stone but out of it: out of love of a First Nations sculpture keeping him company for several decades now.

Laurie Lewis

Laurie Lewis is a Fellow of the Graphic Designers of Canada and is editor and art director of *Vista*, the magazine of the Seniors Association in Kingston, Ontario. Her work has been on CBC and has been published in *Contemporary Verse 2*, *Queen's Feminist Review*, and *Kingston Poets' Gallery*. A chapter of her current manuscript was shortlisted for the 2007 CBC Literary Awards in Creative Non-Fiction.

Laurie's grandmother, Charlotte Fox, was orphaned in Scotland at twelve. She worked as a skivy to care for her younger brother, Sam, who had inherited the family house. When she was sixteen, she married John Anderson from Glasgow. They immigrated to Canada with Sam, to a farm outside Vancouver. With no birth control available, Charlotte had a baby every two years for 20 years. Her 10 children were all born in October or November – the result, she said, of Canada's cold winters.

Rebecca Luce-Kapler

Rebecca Luce-Kapler is Professor of Language and Literacy in the Faculty of Education, Queen's University at Kingston, Ontario. Her book, *Writing With, Through and Beyond the Text: An Ecology of Language,* brings together her work with women writers and her understanding of learning, writing, and teaching. She has published fiction and poetry in a number of literary magazines and anthologies and is the author of a collection of poetry, *The Gardens Where She Dreams.*

The grandmother that Rebecca wrote about is her grandmother's older sister, Emily. Emily clearly remembered the family escaping from Russia at the end of the 19th century (when Czar Nicholas was taking away the religious freedoms of the Moravians and pressing them into military service). When Rebecca was sixteen, she interviewed Emily about this experience and has been fascinated with her story ever since.

Kathryn MacDonald

Kathryn MacDonald's poems have been published in literary journals such as *Descant, The Fiddlehead,* and *Northward Journal* (under the name Deneau) before she took a hiatus from poetry to work at *Harrowsmith* and *Equinox* magazines. Since then, Kathryn has worked as a ghostwriter, editor, and article writer, including *Voices from the Edge of the Island,* a story that focuses on Grandma Lily and the loss of culture, which was published in *This Magazine* during the 500th anniversary of Christopher Columbus' "discovery" of the "New World," and who is the inspiration for the poems in this anthology. Essays on rurality and food were published in *The Farm and City Cookbook* (co-authored with Mary Lou Morgan, Second Story Press). When Kathryn isn't writing or offering online and weekend workshops, she transforms stones into amulets and pendants. A collection of poetry and a novella are currently with a publisher.

Author's note for poem page 42: the Kiowa poet is N. Scott Momaday, from the Forward to Keepers of the Earth, (Michael J. Caduto and Joseph Bruchac. Golden, Colorado: Fullcrum, Inc., 1988)

D.S. Martin

D.S. Martin is the author of the poetry chapbook, *So The Moon Would Not Be Swallowed* (Rubicon Press, 2007), which describes the experiences of his grandparents who were missionaries to China from 1923 to 1951. In *Routines and Recurrences,* Martin writes about his wife's grandmother living in North Bay, Ontario, who will be 98 at the time of this anthology's printing. His new poetry collection, *Poiema,* will be published by Wipf & Stock in 2008.

Kathleen M. Martin

Kathleen expresses her thoughts and feelings best through the written word. Her history teacher told her, 'You write much better than you speak.' Kathleen knew any praise from Miss Nelson always held a dose of criticism, but this time her assessment was true.

Kathleen's published works are *Time of Trial: Beyond the Terror of 9/11*, *Signatures*, *I Lost Me* and *The Bathhouse*, in print and as a reading on CBC.

Upon retirement, Kathleen took writing more seriously. Winning a membership in the Writers' Circle of Durham Region invested Kathleen with a wealth of knowledge. Over the past 8 years, she has served on the Board; attended retreats; participated in courses for Freefall Writing and met regularly with other published authors. Kathleen's manuscript of fictional stories entitled *Keeping the Peace* is now complete. Kathleen believes she inherited her granny's most influential trait, that of character building.

Louise O'Donnell

Louise O'Donnell has a B.A. in creative writing from York University, has studied at Sage Hill Writing Experience in Saskatchewan, and was a participant in the League of Canadian Poets Mentorship Program. In 1990, Louise moved from Toronto, Ontario to Prince Edward County. She has had poems published in journals and anthologies across Canada and abroad, has several chapbooks in print, and in 2003, collaborated with Wayne McNulty to produce *Infinite Horizons*, poems inspired by Wayne's photographs.

Louise's most recent book of poems, *Shuffling into Place*, was published in March 2005 and subsequently developed into a dramatic piece, which was included in the 2005 Horn Trip, a theatre festival performed in venues around Prince Edward County.

The poems in this anthology honour a strong, loving, independent, creative woman: her maternal grandmother. Louise believes that while her grandmother died when she was eleven, this strong woman's influence continues to guide her.

Ann Peacock

Ann is an Oshawa resident who is pursuing her lifelong interest in writing. She is the leader of Inkspot writing circle, as well as being a member of Writers' Circle of Durham Region, Circle for Children's Writers, the Ontario Poetry Society/Oshawa, and Toastmasters International. Ann has a passion for poetry, but writes short fiction and articles as well. Her future plans include writing novels and non-fiction books. Her dream is to die at age 100 in the middle of creating a poem.

Ann did not have a grandmother. Her poem is a composite of the ones she has met and the ones she has imagined as her own.

John Pigeau

John Pigeau is a Kingston-area author and journalist. His first novel, *The Journals of Templeton Speck*, will be set for publication in the summer of 2008. *A Very Good Soul* is a fictionalized account of John's last visit with his beloved grandmother, Lulu Hazel Chapman, who passed away at the age of 95 in June 2007. A woman of extraordinary strength and kindness, Lulu (pronounced *Lula*) lived most of her life in North Bay, working at a photographer's studio and at various department stores, while raising Anna, her only daughter, with whom she shared an astonishingly beautiful bond. When she retired in 1980, Lulu moved to Kingston to be nearer her daughter and grandchildren. She was quick with a smile, made friends at every turn, and was living proof that one person can make the world a better place through the simple act of human kindness.

R.D. Roy

R.D. Roy was raised and educated in Montreal, Quebec. His mixed anglo/francophone heritage and working-class background are often reflected in his writing.

He has been a featured reader at the Kingston Dub Poetry Festival, the Dub/Kingston Poets' Solidarity Tour, The Al Purdy People's Poetry Festival, the Havana International Book Festival and has performed at Hot-Sauced Words and the Art Bar in Toronto, Ontario.

Roy is a member of the Canada Cuba Literary Alliance and PEN Canada. Now living near Kingston, Ontario, he has been a regular reader in area coffeehouses and at local poetry events. His work was included in *Scapes: Poetry & Company, A Kingston Community Anthology* and Montreal's *Matrix* magazine.

Roy's first book of poetry, *Three Cities*, was released by Hidden Brook Press in early 2008.

K.V. Skene

Born in Sault Ste. Marie, Ontario, K.V. Skene lived in Lachine, Quebec, Toronto and Colborne, Ontario, and Victoria, B.C. before departing for the U.K. and Ireland. Currently, she is happily ensconced in Oxford, England.

Skene's poetry has appeared in Canadian, U.K., U.S., Irish, Australian and Austrian magazines. Publications include *Only a Dragon* and *Calendar of Rain*, winners of the 2002 and 2004 Shaunt Basmajian Chapbook Award (Canada); a chapbook, *Edith* (a series of poems on Nurse Edith Cavell), courtesy of Flarestack Publishing (U.K.) and her latest book, *Love in the (Irrational) Imperfect*, published by Hidden Brook Press (Canada).

Translating Grandma and *For an Old Woman Who Carried On* were inspired by Skene's paternal grandmother who, with unflagging devotion, took in her grandchildren after their mother died in childbirth. The grandmother in *Grandmother's Children* was an elderly lady who was the babysitter of choice (and adopted grandmother) for an entire neighbourhood.

Ruth E. Walker

1918: Gram on the Danforth was inspired by an oft-told tale of Ruth's grandmother, Clara Brooks, about the horrific days at the height of the Spanish flu epidemic. Clara nursed her gravely ill mother back to health through instinct— "Those oranges," she used to say. "I think it must have been those oranges." Typical of Ruth's beloved Gram, she never gave herself credit.

Ruth E. Walker is a poet, writer, playwright and editor. Her work has appeared in publications as diverse as *Contemporary Verse 2*, *Canadian Living*, and *River King Poetry Supplement* (US). Poetry is forthcoming in the Scottish journal *Chapman*, and an in-progress play is being workshopped in the 2007/08 season of Stone Circle Theatre in Ajax. Ruth was named recently as one of four artists in residence through the Ontario Arts Council for a high school pilot project with the Durham District School Board. Ruth lives and writes in Whitby, Ontario.

Anne Watson-Russell, B.A., M.Ed., Ph.D.

Anne Watson-Russell has lived and taught in foreign countries and traveled around the world. She has been an award-winning community actress and Special Education Resource Teacher, a University Professor, a Psycho-Educational Consultant and the mother of two beautiful, high-needs children (one born with too little dopamine, the other born with too much shopping gene). Anne has weathered great joy and great sadness in perhaps equal measure. Being a grandmother is the surprise reward.

Carolyn Wilker

Carolyn Wilker of Kitchener, Ontario is a freelance writer, editor, and speaker. Her early years were spent on a farm that was formerly owned by her paternal grandparents. When the author was very young, her grandparents moved to Stratford, where they lived at the time of this story. *Anticipated Visits* relates a yearning to spend more time with this grandmother Carolyn saw less often.

Publication credits include book reviews, articles, and opinion editorials in *Canada Lutheran*, *The Record*, *Esprit*, and *Glad Tidings*; devotionals in *Eternity for Today*, *Esprit*, *Upper Room*, and *Glad Tidings*; and poetry in *Tower Poetry*, *Esprit*, *Glad Tidings*, *Tickled by Thunder*, *Favourite Poems Contest Anthology* (Craigleigh Press), *Writers Undercover*, and *Voices and Visions*.

Carolyn's editing and proofreading work is predominantly non-fiction and has included business newsletters, the *Africa Bible Commentary*, non-fiction and poetry manuscripts, website content, promotional material, and articles.

Carolyn Hei-Kyoung You

Carolyn Hei-Kyoung You is a writer who lives in Kingston, Ontario. Her previous publishing credits include a submission to Carol Krause's anthology *Between Myself and Them: Stories of Disability and Difference*, Second Story Press 2005.

Among Carolyn's spiritual affiliations are The Art of Living Foundation, Soulful Singing, Sydenham Street United Church, and Transfiguration Church.

Carolyn visited the Republic of Korea with her father in 1999. In 2004, she attended the Women and Peacebuilding in Korea Conference convened by the Canada-DPR Korea Association. Writing this piece has reignited her interest in all things Korean. She hopes one day to be able to read, in the original Korean, the book that her maternal grandfather wrote in memory of his wife. Carolyn loves her mother's homemade japchae and enjoys the occasional bowl of kimchi jjigae.

Ruth Zaryski Jackson

Ruth Zaryski Jackson never knew her own grandmothers — one stayed in Ukraine, and the other died when Ruth was two. Born in Toronto, Ruth spent her first nine years living in a downtown rooming house where Sadie was the first of several older women to whom she found herself irresistibly drawn.

In the 1960's, Ruth returned from the suburbs to her old neighbourhood, attending the University of Toronto where she studied Anthropology. After working in research, teaching, heritage planning, and raising three small children, Ruth turned from writing reports to writing non-fiction. This story, originally conceived in a memoir-writing course, is part of a larger memoir on which she is currently working, excavating the layers of her immigrant family's history and weaving together the threads of the generations. Ruth and her husband live on a farm near Mount Albert, Ontario with their Black Lab, Toby.